LIFE AND ITS MARVELS

LIFE AND ITS MARVELS:

PLANT, ANIMAL, HUMAN

The International Pictorial Treasury of Knowledge

INTERNATIONAL GRAPHIC SOCIETY

ENGLEWOOD CLIFFS, NEW JERSEY

Contents

Introduction

by JOSEPH LAUWERYS, D. Sc., D. Lit.

OUR ancestors, millions of years ago, were as much a part of Nature as any sheep or moth or blade of grass. They moved towards and swallowed their food or water, just as they breathed the air, without taking thought and without being aware of what they were doing. Of course they made mistakes—sometimes the fruits they ate killed instead of nourishing, or the water they drank gave loathsome diseases. But man learns more quickly from experience than do the beasts of the field and he can hand on to his fellows and to his descendants an increasing stock of knowledge. He broods over this stock, rejecting some, treasuring the rest. Seeing someone suffer or even die after eating scarlet berries or after being bitten by a particular kind of snake he learns to treat both with fear and respect and teaches his children to avoid them.

Primitive man, living in caves half-a-million years ago, already knew much about plants and animals, though in a rough, unsystematic way. He was still part of Nature, as indeed we ourselves are but, through his reasoning power and his social sense, was beginning to think of himself as in some ways apart from and even opposed to his surroundings. The notion that Nature and the World offered a field for exploration was coming to birth and was beginning to spread. Yet it is only during the last few thousand years that this new idea has begun to be truly effective and only during the last four hundred that it has been pursued with clarity and continuity. In Alexandria, under the Ptolemies who succeeded Alexander the Great about 300 B.C., there existed a museum in which research workers were supplied with a zoo, a botanical garden and laboratories. They pursued their inquiries in the spirit of the Greek Aristotle, the first of the great biologists—"In every natural object, in every living thing, there is something to excite our admiration; in every one some part of nature, some element of beauty. If anybody should despise the study of other living creatures as unworthy of attention, let him think the same of himself, for it is not possible without great disgust to contemplate the elements of which man is made—the blood, the flesh, the bones, the veins and all such parts."

The stock of living forms revealed by careful exploration is tremendous in its variety. Leaving aside the whole kingdom of plants, biologists list more than 250,000 different species of animals. Of these, more than half are insects, those tiny beings which continue to dispute our dominion, while there are over 14,000 kinds of birds. The differences in size are prodigious—there are gigantic whales sixty feet long and weighing a hundred tons while at the other extreme there are numberless creatures, of exquisitely complex structure, far too small to be seen with the naked eye. Think too of the range of architectural design; compare the worm and the lion, the snail and the bird, the blade of grass and the giant redwood tree of California. What a world it is! What wealth, beauty and variety! What occasions for wonder and delight!

Obviously not all forms of life are useful to mankind. Yet if we made a full and exhaustive survey of all the plants, animals and microorganisms upon which we depend for our lives, we should certainly be astounded.

The second great motive for the study of life in its manifold variety is our desire to be healthy and free of disease. That the leaves or roots of some plants serve as purgatives or help wounds to heal or assuage fever were early discoveries and a knowledge of such simple remedies would be part of the stock-in-trade of medicine men and priests. Again, knowledge of human anatomy would help the first doctors to set a broken limb or even to attempt surgical operations for the removal of painful growths or diseased organs. Dissections were much used thousands of years ago to train medical men in the ancient empires of Egypt, Mesopotamia, China and India.

Our debt, however, is greater to the doctors of ancient Greece. Their greatest contribution was the discovery of a method of research which we still apply—that of patient observation together with common-sense reasoning. Like modern investigators, the Greeks attempted always to explain natural phenomena by natural causes—they were as suspicious of explanations in terms of demons or spirits as we are ourselves.

This is surely the right approach to the study of life. Thanks to it a long line of men of genius have been able to build up slowly and patiently the staggering and monumental edifice of modern science. Thanks to it we have more than doubled the average expectation of life and we, moreover, maintain in health and vigor the vast numbers of humans who now inhabit the planet and are transforming its surface. The surgeons of today, able to manipulate the living heart or brain, the research workers who discovered wonder drugs like insulin, penicillin and aureomycin, to mention only a few, are the direct successors of those early scientists.

We must not, however, exaggerate the knowledge possessed by our predecessors. On reading a book such as this—*Life and its Marvels*—it is astonishing to think how much of the material gathered in it is new, novel, modern—based upon the findings of the last one hundred years, and a great deal of it far more recent than that. It is a treasure-house of knowledge; in ancient Greece it would have been worth many times its weight in gold while in the Middle Ages it would have been either condemned as the work of the devil or, perhaps, revered as the revelation of the Word of God.

Since we have not yet, as a species, learned fully to control for good purposes the knowledge we have attained, particularly that concerning the structure of the nuclei of atoms, there is a real danger that our civilization and our culture may be destroyed.

Some people have therefore suggested that we should promptly set about building modern Noah's Arks—repositories of Man's knowledge and achievements, buried deep in the hearts of mountains. When the flood of war and destruction had receded, civilization could start again from such centers. Were such an idea realized, then surely books like this are fully deserving of a place in the Ark. They would present to the survivors knowledge that could be immediately put to use and would be a monument of human achievement.

For it should be clear that, if we understand the mechanisms which enable animals to function, we are at once in a position to keep ourselves more fit and healthy. Widespread knowledge of a kind that could easily be spread through the study of lively and appealing books like this one would turn many miserable hypochondriacs into cheerful, vigorous men and women, enjoying life to the full.

Nevertheless, not many of us, as we spend pleasant hours with the pictures gathered here, will think in the first instance of the use to which we shall put the facts we are learning. Surely our first reaction will be simple amazement at the endless complexity and beauty of the universe of life. Out of this wonder problems arise—what is Life itself? Could we ourselves create it out of dead matter? How do the parents hand down to their young their own shape and substance? What really distinguishes living stuff from stones or crystals?

Even the most learned find it hard or impossible to answer such questions. What is Life? We can certainly describe some of the characteristics which distinguish living beings from stones—but is that enough? And even then the answers are not very precise. The great Linnaeus, for instance, more than two hundred years ago said that "Stones grow, plants grow, the live animals grow and live and feel." But we now think he was not as wise in saying this as he usually was. For plants, we now know, certainly feel while stones do not grow in the sense that animals do. The latter take in matter from the air or the soil or from other living things and then change this matter very much, indeed, into quite different substances by a power of their own. Nor do they simply get bigger in size, keeping their shape. They go through a whole cycle of development. Again, living things—and apparently only living things—can learn to profit by experience, that is they can adapt their functioning to changing circumstances, storing the lessons of the past as a guide to the future. If a starfish is turned upside down and then, after a good deal of trying, manages to right itself it will manage to achieve this result much more quickly next time it is put upon its back. At a higher level, animals like rats and chimpanzees display intelligent behavior, analogous to that of man, as they learn to tread mazes or to reach out after bananas. How different from the behavior of stones or clouds!

We can extend our list of the characteristics of living things, but as we go on we would certainly come across some real puzzles. There are some forms of matter which are a bridge between the living and the non-living. Only a very bold and very silly man would dare to put boundaries to the future achievements of science. So far, it seems certain that every living thing comes only from another living thing, every cell from a cell. Was it ever thus? Are we forced to assume the direct act of creation by God? Or did God allow natural laws and processes to operate over uncountable millions of years during which Life emerged from the water and the slime?

The general picture is fairly clear and it is widely accepted. But the real detail is still lacking. Much remains to be found out about the laws of heredity and of change as well as about the mechanism of evolution. But we can surely see, opening before us, the prospect of decisively intervening so as to produce new species more suited to our needs or more pleasing to our senses than those we know already.

In a modest way, gardeners and breeders of animals have long held this sort of aim before themselves. They have achieved noteworthy successes. Cows, pigs, sheep are larger and better providers of meat or milk than they were two hundred years ago. Flowers are brighter and more colorful. Fruit, too, has been improved by men like Luther Burbank who produced cherries, apricots, peaches and so on to suit the specifications and the needs of the canning industry. But this sort of thing is only a mere beginning. Full knowledge of heredity and its laws as well as of the process of evolution could enable us to achieve results which would be as different from what has been done as a jet plane is from a kite or an ocean liner from a dugout canoe.

And then at last would open out the prospect of influencing the evolution of man himself so that he would gradually become a being who would more fully embody the potentialities of our species than we ourselves do; who would be, so to speak, a nobler and more beautiful and wiser man than we are. But this is as yet far off in the future and our present concern must be to tame the beast within us so that it does not destroy both us and our achievements.

Here then are just a few of the possibilities which modern biologists, students of life and of the history of Nature, see opening up. Here are a few of the problems which they are endeavoring to tackle. Those who read and study this book will surely find in it delight and excitement. They will be able, too, to share in a humble and modest way in the great adventure of ideas which modern science is. The aim is to endow mankind with fresh powers and new insights. Success comes as the reward of patience, modesty, hard work and vigorous thinking. We can all share a little in what is going on and we must be grateful to have the opportunity of understanding and learning. That is why I hope that you will be encouraged not only to go on learning biology when you have finished reading this book but that you will also go out into the fields to see with your own eyes. Go out and look and observe. Get hold of a microscope if you can or, if not, get a magnifying glass. Science is something you must learn for and by yourself and it is something you must do with your own hands—it can never be learned from books alone. Watch and cultivate a patch of garden, keep pets and watch them, note how farm animals are fed and cared for. Try to repeat some of the experiments you will read about in this book or others like it. Then turn again to books and they will help you to make your knowledge more useful and orderly, more meaningful and satisfying by showing how the results of observations and experiments can all be fitted together into a pattern of growing intricacy and beauty.

Cells - the Building Bricks of Life

Can you believe your eyes? Do they tell you the truth, the whole truth and nothing but the truth? One thing you can be sure of. They scarcely ever tell the whole truth. When you look out to sea your eyes may tell you that a small blob and a wisp of smoke mean a ship on the horizon. But they will not tell you whether it is a small trawler or a giant liner. To find that out you need a powerful telescope. Look at a drop of tap water and a drop of clear pond water. Are they both equally clean? To find that out you need a powerful microscope.

Until about four hundred years ago nothing resembling a modern microscope existed. Then various spectacle makers in Holland noticed that when certain kinds of lenses are used in pairs and at the right distance apart they greatly magnify things. About 1660, seventy years or so after the first discovery, Robert Hooke used the magnifying instrument shown on the opposite page. To help him see things even better, he focused the light of a candle on his specimens by means of a glass globe filled with water.

Hooke's instrument was scarcely powerful enough to be called a microscope, but it did enable him to see things that nobody had noticed before. One day he examined a thin slice of cork. He was amazed to find that it was made up of a great number of tiny divisions, rather like a honeycomb. With that in mind, he gave these divisions the name of cells. He had no idea then just how important that word was to become when microscopes improved and scientists were better able to see and study living things.

The first man to make really powerful microscopes was a Dutch draper named Leeuwenhoek, who was born in 1632. His instruments were capable of magnifying things to two or three hundred times their actual size. Below his portrait

opposite, you can see one of his simplest microscopes and how a very small insect looked when seen through it.

Leeuwenhoek saw many living things that no man had ever seen before. In water where he had allowed some hay to ferment, he discovered creatures which were later given the name protozoa, from two Greek words meaning first (or most primitive) animals. In one of the many interesting letters which he wrote to naturalists and learned societies he declared that even though he gargled with salt water every day, the number of little animals in his mouth was greater than the whole population of Holland.

Although Leeuwenhoek did not know it, many of the "little animals" he discovered consisted of only a single cell, the name which scientists now give to the smallest complete unit of living matter, the very building bricks of life. Just before 1940 two German naturalists proved that all plants and all animals are made up entirely of living cells. Some consist of only one cell, others of many millions.

Cells themselves vary greatly in size and shape. It would take anything between 250 and 2500 of certain common kinds, packed side by side, to stretch across the width of a quarter. But there are some cells larger than that and some far smaller. The size of an animal tells us nothing about the size of the cells which make it up. The huge elephant is not made of larger cells than the small field mouse. It is simply made of more cells.

If all the cells of one human body could be turned into ordinary building bricks, there would be enough to build a wall as wide and as high as the Great Wall of China, and long enough to stretch around the equator seventeen times.

TOP LEFT: Leeuwenhoek, his microscope, and a sample of what it showed. BELOW: The early magnifier which revealed the cells in cork. TOP RIGHT: The wall which the cells of your body could build if each were a real brick. (A) Individual cell; (B) Group of cells; (C) The cells in a single human body.

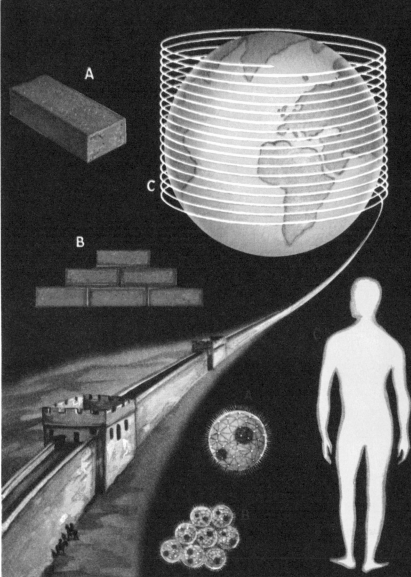

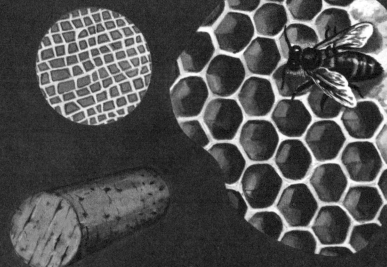

Modern Microscopes look inside a Single Cell

Not only have microscopes improved out of all knowledge since Leeuwenhoek's time, but we have also developed far better means of lighting and have greatly improved the methods of preparing specimens for microscopic examination. In addition, the art of photography now allows us to keep permanent records of what the microscope reveals and to show them, enlarged still further, on a screen. As a result, the modern scientist can not only see single cells, he can actually look inside them and see what these bricks of life are made of.

Here we can note how he sets to work to see inside the cells of a leaf. He cannot see the whole leaf at once under his microscope and, indeed, he does not want to. But before taking a small piece (1) for examination he first treats the whole leaf with certain chemicals which make it less opaque so that light can pass through it. Next he plunges it into a paraffin bath to harden it. Now, with a microtome (which simply means an instrument for cutting very small things) he cuts off the very fine slice he needs (2). Then, with a special adhesive, he fixes it to one thin glass slide and covers it with another one, probably using the kind of apparatus shown in picture 3.

He can now examine his specimen in several different ways. If he wishes, he can use twin microscopes (4a) which enable him to see it by direct light, but which do not magnify as greatly as other microscopes. But this method is used mainly for examining objects through which light cannot pass; so to examine a fine and almost transparent layer of leaf he would probably use the kind of microscope shown in (4b). This is fitted with a mirror which reflects the light from a lamp onto the specimen from below. He may even use a similar microscope fitted with a special camera (4c) so that he can make a photographic slide and show it on a screen.

He now has a very large picture showing a score or more of leaf cells, like that shown opposite. Perhaps the most noticeable thing about them is that they are separated from one another by firm "cell walls" (A), made of a hard, woody substance called cellulose. Most plant cells have these hard walls, but animal cells do not. That is probably why plant cells are easier to see and were discovered before animal cells.

The bulk of the contents of each cell is a colorless, transparent jelly (B) called protoplasm, which means "first form of matter". This substance, which we may think of as the prime substance of life, is present in living cells but not in dead ones. Chemists who have analyzed protoplasm tell us that in addition to water and salts, it contains fats, substances like egg-white called albuminoids, and substances similar to starch and sugar, called carbohydrates. When the chemist analyzes protoplasm he cannot avoid destroying it as living matter. But if a cell wall is carefully pricked, protoplasm may trickle out and it is sometimes possible to see a movement of circulation inside.

In the protoplasm of each cell there is one specially important part (C) called the nucleus. It is separated from the protoplasm only by a very, very fine skin or membrane. With an extremely powerful microscope it is possible see a fine grain-like substance inside the nucleus called chromatin.

The tiny green discs (D) in the protoplasm of leaf cells are made of chlorophyll. Chlorophyll is found only in plant cells, and only in those parts of the plant which are exposed to light. In sunlight, this chlorophyll enables the plant to turn water from the soil and carbon dioxide from the air into food.

TOP: Preparing a slice of leaf for the microscope. CENTER: Three methods of microscopic examination. BOTTOM: Magnified pictures of leaf cells.

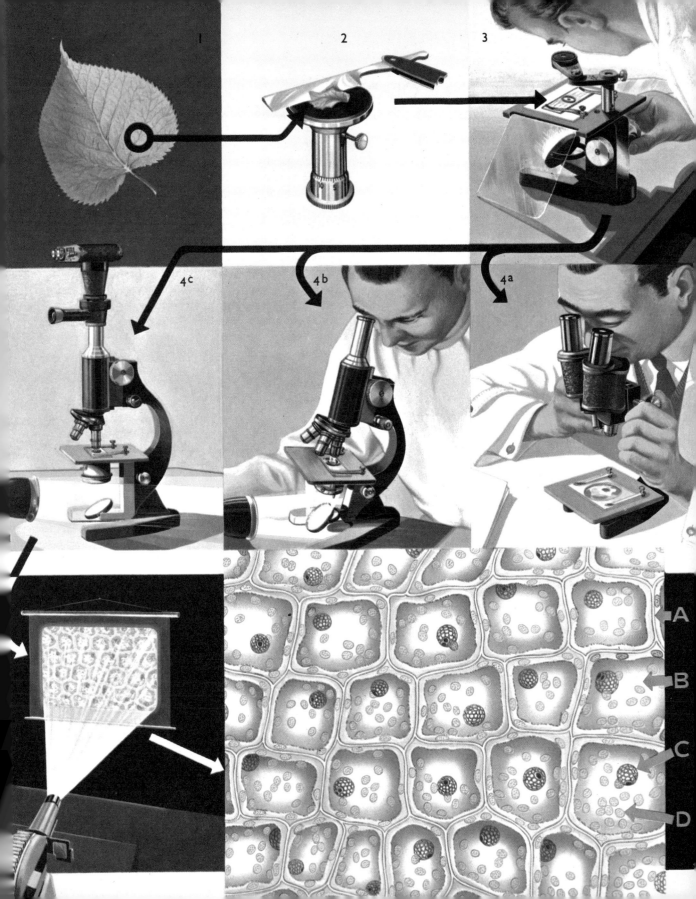

1

2

3

4c

4b

4a

A

B

C

D

How one Unit of Life becomes two

Two of the most important features which distinguish living things from inanimate things like stones and metal are their ability to grow and to reproduce creatures like themselves. These features are present not only in all the big, familiar animals and plants but also in the very smallest unit of life, the cell. In the course of growth a cell may eventually reach about double its normal size. Then, possibly in a few minutes, possibly over several hours, according to what kind of cell it is, it splits into two. Each of the two new cells is a complete unit of life, and each is about the same size as the original one was before its outburst of growth.

With the help of the top six pictures on the opposite page we can follow what happens during the process of division. First we see the original cell, with its nucleus containing the grain-like substance called chromatin, and we notice a tiny speck (A) at the side of the nucleus, called the centriole. Next we see that this centriole has split into two parts (B), each surrounded by a sort of halo of fine threads. Meanwhile, the chromatin has ceased to be a mass of tiny grains and has arranged itself as a number of fine, hair-like spirals called chromosomes, which simply means colored bodies.

In the third picture there are even more dramatic changes. The two halves of the centriole are moving further and further apart towards the "poles" of the cell and their haloes have touched the chromosomes. These have begun to move towards the middle of the nucleus (D) and each one has split into two, lengthwise (E). The fine membrane which formerly surrounded the nucleus, separating it from the protoplasm outside, has begun to dissolve and disappear (C).

Now the cell begins to change shape, becoming longer and narrower. The two centrioles have reached opposite ends of the cell and exactly half the bundle of chromosomes seems to have been drawn towards each of them (F). Next, both groups of chromosomes seem to begin wrapping themselves around (G), and the whole cell shows signs of breaking into two (H). Last, the chromosomes have turned into grain-like masses of chromatin once more, and around each of the two masses a new skin, or nuclear membrane, is beginning to form. There are now two complete and perfect cells, ready to break apart and live as two separate units of life.

Different species of animals (and of plants) have different numbers of chromosomes in their cells. The fly, for example, has six and the carp a hundred and four. The potato has forty-eight.

It is not possible to find any other process which compares exactly with the wonderful division of a living cell in every respect, but what happens inside a tulip bulb is similar in at least some ways. The bulb gives a fine flower in spring (1) only because it is like a storehouse packed with food. If it is to give a flower again next year, it must be kept in the soil (2) so that its roots can take in nourishment and enable it to build up a fresh food-reserve. While it lies in the soil, a "replacement bulb" (3A) forms inside it, and often, too, a kind of immature or "offset" bulb (3B) forms as well.

In summer, when the flower fades (4), it is often possible to extract both the replacement bulb and the offset bulb, and to plant both of them (5). Both can then live their own separate lives, producing two new flowers (6). So just as one cell gives rise to two cells, so one tulip bulb can also give rise to two tulip bulbs.

ABOVE: How a single living cell divides into two living cells. BELOW: How a single bulb can give rise to two bulbs, each able to produce a new flower.

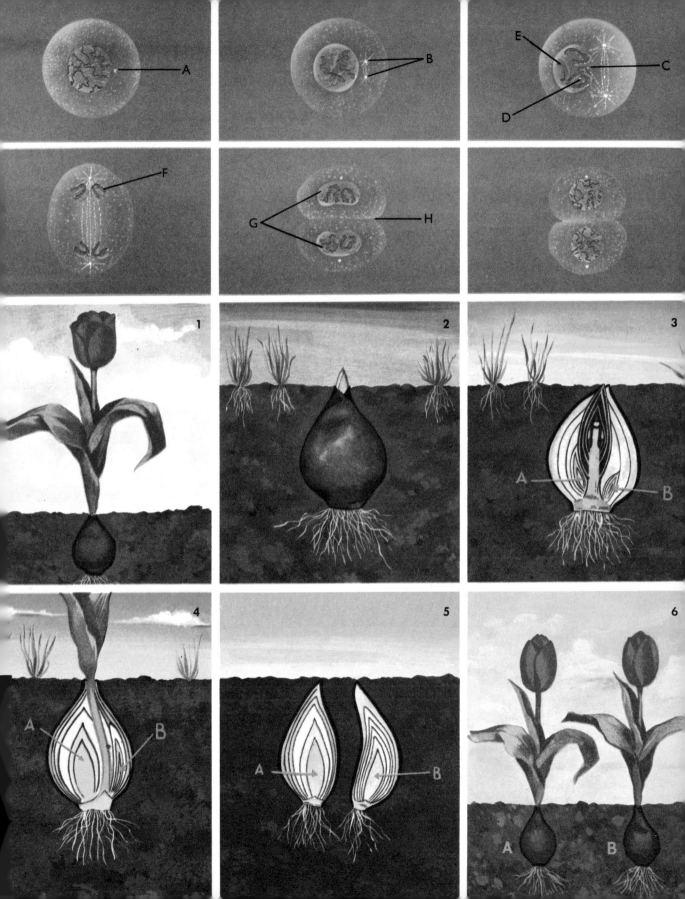

What Living means to every Creature

However different all the many thousands of plants and animals may be from one another, there are at least four things which every one of them must be able to do to keep life going. They must all be able to move, to obtain and use food, to grow, and to create new beings like themselves. All these things are part of the very meaning of life, even to the smallest and simplest of living creatures, though different creatures tackle these problems in different ways.

The single-cell ameba, opposite, does all these things without limbs, without any kind of nervous system, and without any specialized organs of digestion or reproduction. It is little more than a small mass of jelly-like protoplasm, of no fixed shape, with a nucleus. Some kinds of ameba live in ponds or ditches and, in times of severe drought, wrap themselves in a protective envelope until the water returns. Others live as parasites in the bodies of men or animals, sometimes causing serious diseases.

The top picture (A) shows how the ameba moves without limbs. It can squeeze its own jelly-like substance into many different shapes, so that at any moment various parts may jut out in various directions. The parts that jut out at any particular moment are called pseudopodia, from two Greek words meaning "false feet". In the second part of picture A, the ameba has squeezed its whole tiny body together to follow the advance of the false foot.

It would be a mistake to think that the ameba's movements are a mere mechanical process and nothing more. Just as there are reasons why we sometimes walk, sometimes run and sometimes change direction, so there are reasons why the ameba moves in different ways at different times.

If we touch one of its false feet with a needle while it is moving forward, the ameba will either stop moving or else change its direction. It may completely withdraw the "foot" we touch, and push out another one on the opposite side. It may even be stimulated to change its course by means of certain chemicals. So although it has no nervous system, it is doubtless capable of some sort of feeling.

Next we see how the ameba feeds without a mouth (B). Any part of its body surface can absorb soft food particles. Let us assume that the yellow speck is a minute single-cell plant. The ameba pushes out two pseudopodia and wraps them around it. The minute plant is then absorbed into the ameba's body. There, by means of highly complicated chemical changes which are not yet fully understood, part is transformed into protoplasm for growth, and part converted into energy for movement. Any waste matter is expelled from the ameba's body.

The growth of the ameba (C) is not just a question of getting bigger and bigger, as a snowball does when rolled in the snow. Like every other living thing, the ameba grows only because it can turn food substances into a very part of itself. Like other living things, too, it changes in other ways while growing. As the ameba grows, perhaps the most important change is the lengthening of its nucleus.

We saw on the last page what that change foreshadows. In the bottom picture we see how, as the ameba reaches its greatest size, it divides into two, each a complete ameba like the original one, and each indistinguishable from the other.

If every ameba multiplied unchecked in this way the whole earth would soon be populated by them: 1,000,000 would become 2,000,000, then 4,000,000, then 8,000,000 and so on. But in fact, though few of them die a natural death, countless numbers are constantly eaten by larger water-dwelling animals.

How the ameba moves without limbs (A), eats without a mouth (B), changes during growth (C), and turns into two identical creatures (D).

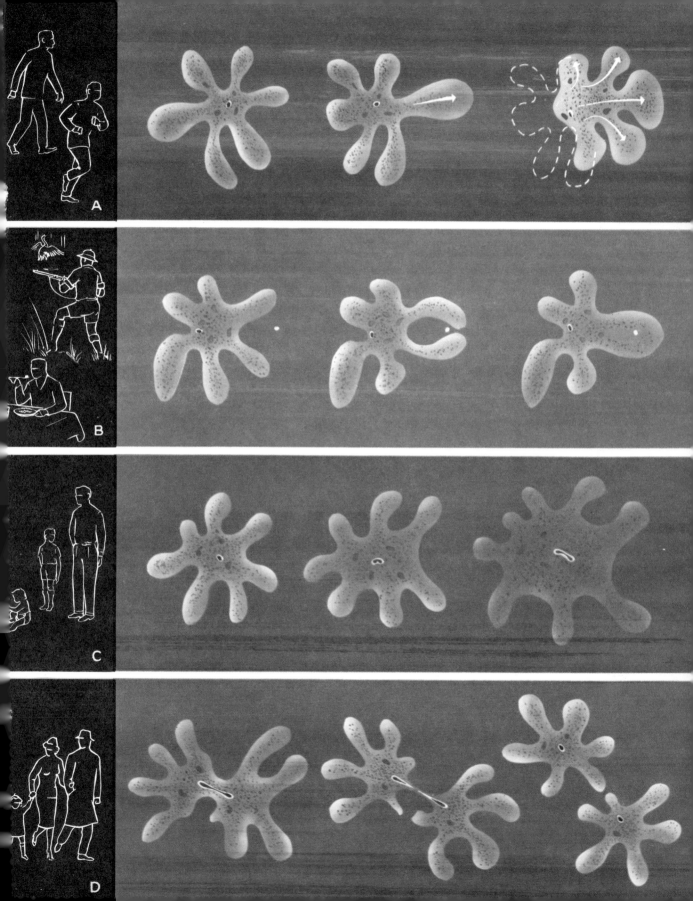

Colonies of Cells with Specialist Workers

In some ways the single-cell ameba is rather like Robinson Crusoe on his lonely island. It has to do everything for itself, just as he had to. When large numbers of human beings live together in towns and cities they no longer behave like Robinson Crusoe. It pays far better for different people to specialize in whatever work they can do best, some preparing food, others building houses, others providing transportation, and so on. The same is very often true of cells when they come together to form large colonies.

In the very simplest cell colonies, which include various kinds of seaweed, there is little or no specialization of labor. When individual cells split into two they merely remain clinging to each other instead of separating. Each cell still does everything for itself, but as the colony grows all feel the benefit of living together. The whole colony can float near the surface of the sea far better than any individual member could alone, and there, in the sunlight, each cell is better able to use its chlorophyll to make its own food.

But there are many other kinds of simple colonies in which different cells begin to do specialized jobs. One kind, called the *volvox globator,* is shown greatly enlarged at the top left of the opposite page. It is a pale greenish ball, measuring about one twenty-fifth of an inch across, and is made up of about ten thousand separate single-cell creatures. Each of these has a tiny hair-like whip, and the lashing of many such whips propels the colony through the fresh water where it lives. Some of the cells, which make up what is called the pole of the colony, have a small, luminous red point, and these cells act as pilots, directing which way the whole colony shall move. Other cells, near the center of the colony, special-ize in reproduction.

Many kinds of cell colonies which live in water are made up entirely of animal cells, yet look very much like plants. One is the sea-fan which lives in the warm seas near the West Indies and which sometimes grows to the size of a small tree. Another is the obelia, which looks like a branch-ing plant carrying two different kinds of bud. The "buds" with feelers catch food for the plant and those without reproduce new cells. In the plant-like colony at the bottom left, called the *Dinobryon sertularia,* we can see newly-formed cells floating away, ready to found new colonies of their own. The coral polyps (bottom right), are composed of many tiny animals, some with tentacles which enable them to catch food, others whose task is to produce new living creatures.

One of the most remarkable examples of labor-specialization in a colony is the Portuguese Man o' War, shown top right. There is little about its appearance to suggest that it is anything other than a kind of large jellyfish with a tangled mass of tentacles — tentacles which, incidentally, can inflict extremely painful stings on any unfortunate swimmer who encounters them. But in fact it is composed of hundreds or even thousands of sepa-rate tiny animals. The key at the side of the picture indicates how different animals in this strange colony perform various jobs which, in our own bodies, are undertaken by many different specialized organs.

The whole colony centers around a main trunk, which carries food to all the "colonists". At its top is a vessel filled with air (1), which serves as a float, and below this is a double row of swimming bells (2). Other animals serve as feelers (3), and yet others (4) and (6) play the part of male and female in reproduction. The tentacles (5) catch food and the polyps (7) pass it on to the main trunk for all to share.

LEFT: Cell colonies in which different cells do different jobs. The top ones are little bigger than a pin's head. RIGHT: The Portuguese Man o' War (above the coral) and a key to the work its member-animals do.

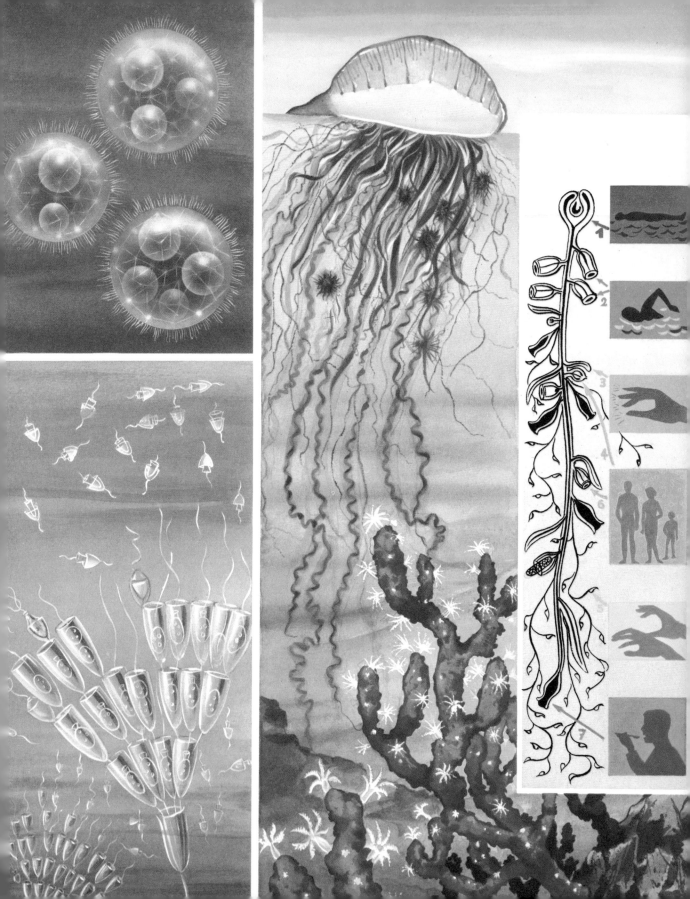

The World of Life in a Drop of Water

Single-cell creatures are not like prehistoric monsters—things which we can only learn about by reading books and visiting museums. Without any very great labor or expense we can see many of them for ourselves and watch exactly how they feed and how they move about. The young man opposite is one of thousands who have made this their hobby, and who find it no more expensive than, say, amateur photography or stamp collecting. He needs very little more than a microscope, with a few accessories, and three or four coloring agents. He can probably find as many specimens as he could wish for in the nearest pond or ditch.

More than twenty thousand *different kinds* of single-cell creatures live in such patches of stagnant water and a great many of them are extremely common. All the enthusiastic naturalist need do is to scoop up a glassful of pond water, preferably from near a spot where water plants are abundant. When he measures out a single drop and places it under his microscope he will find in it a veritable world of living things, forever on the move, such as our middle picture shows.

We have already seen how the ameba moves by means of its strange "false feet", and how other single-cell animals can swim with hair-like whips. Many of the creatures in this world of a drop of water move in quite a different fashion. All or part of the body is covered by very fine threads or lashes which thrash about rapidly and form a current to carry them through the water.

The slipper-shaped paramecium (top left) is completely covered by threads of this kind and, considering its minute size, it is a very fast swimmer indeed. The ameba, even at its fastest, would take something like two-and-a-half to three-and-a-half hours to travel a quarter of an inch. The paramecium can make the same journey in fourteen or fifteen seconds. An inch a minute may not sound very fast, but we are discussing here a very tiny world, and very tiny creatures. Only when we actually witness it through a microscope can we appreciate what an outstanding turn of speed it really is.

The paramecium uses its lashes for other things besides swimming, too. Unlike the ameba, it cannot absorb food through any part of its body-surface, because the outer layer of its protoplasm forms a kind of hard skin which enables the creature to keep its shape. But a small part of its surface is more tender and serves as a primitive kind of mouth through which it must take in whatever nourishment it needs. The paramecium can speed up the movement of the lashes around this mouth to guide food towards it.

Among creatures of its own size the paramecium might well prove a formidable opponent, for in a fraction of a second it can throw out a thick covering of protective hairs around its body.

The stentor (top right), also a swimming creature, can perform even more remarkable feats. It can attach the lower part of its body firmly to a plant and thrust the rest forward in the form of a trumpet. Around the rim of this trumpet there is a spiral of fine hairs, which, by moving rapidly to and fro, draw in food particles.

The bell-shaped vorticella (top center) is rigidly fixed by one end of its body, the foot, to wherever it lives. The unattached end of the body, the head, is covered with a spiral of hairs. Throughout the length of the body protoplasm forms a kind of coil spring which can quite suddenly contract and draw the spiral of hairs, together with the food particles they capture, towards the soft inside where the food can be absorbed.

BELOW: Making ready to study single-cell creatures. CENTER: Part of the world of a drop of water. TOP: Three wonderful minute animals: paramecium, vorticella and stentor.

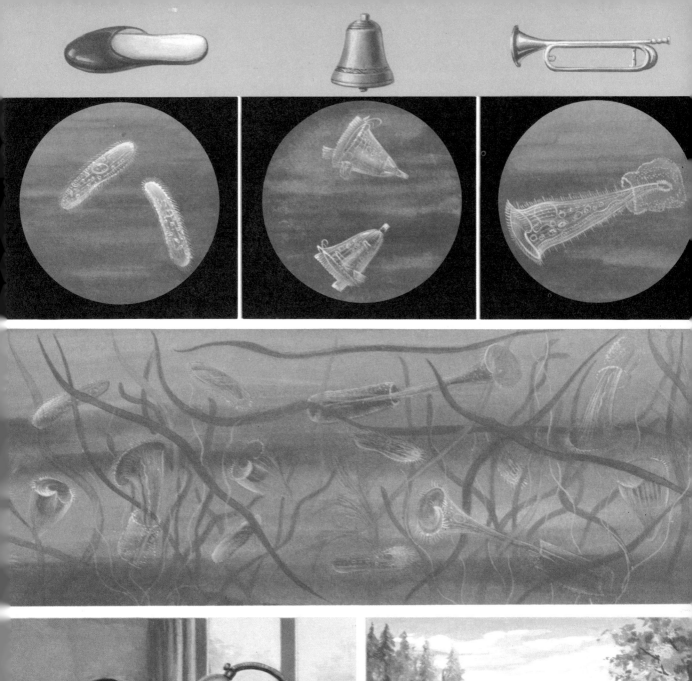
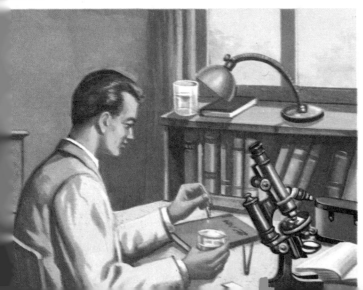

Wonders of Life and Death

Even more strange and wonderful than how they move about and how they feed, is the way in which single-cell animals pass on life. We have seen how the single cell splits into two new living cells, each indistinguishable from the other. When we stop to think about this we notice a remarkable thing. One old cell becomes two *new* cells, each just beginning life and each with an equal chance of later turning into two new cells itself. Were it not that so many single-cell creatures are eaten by larger animals, we might therefore say that they possess the possibility of living indefinitely.

Yet all highly developed animals, even if they escape death from accident, must sooner or later die. Just where does death fit into the wonderful story of life, and what part does it play in that story?

We can get a clue from the volvox, which we saw on page 19, and which is again shown opposite. We noticed that it is made up of many separate single-cell creatures, but that only a small proportion of them, near the center of the colony, specialize in reproduction. In time these specialized cells form a whole new colony inside the old one. Eventually the old colony bursts open and the new one makes its exit into the outside world. The outer cells of the old colony cannot reproduce; they have no possibility of passing on life, and so death makes its appearance.

It seems, then, that for the many benefits which individual cells gain by living together and specializing in different jobs they have to pay this price: only those cells which specialize in reproduction retain the possibility of living indefinitely or of passing life on.

Even so, the life-span of many highly developed creatures is extremely long compared with the short time that most single-cell animals live before they divide into two.

Look at the eleven animals and the one plant pictured opposite. The figure under each shows the maximum number of years it is likely to live. A few species of trees live many, many centuries, but within the animal kingdom there are few creatures which rival mankind, with his possible life-span of a hundred and twenty years.

We can tell nothing about the life-span of an animal merely from its size. The small lobster can expect to live almost as long as the lion, legendary king of beasts, and the elephant, for all its bulk, lives only about a third as long as the tortoise. We can only say in a general way that the life-span of many animals, especially mammals, seems to be about seven times as long as their period of growth.

Few animals living in their wild state actually live as long as our figures show. Most fall victim to some accident which shortens their lives. For instance, an eagle whose eyes were injured at the age of ten would be very unlikely to go on finding sufficient prey to live on for another forty-five years. Yet, put behind the bars of a zoo with its food regularly provided, it might well live that long, even though its life would be more monotonous and less free.

We noticed that in the volvox, while many of the single-cell members of the colony must eventually die, those which specialize in reproduction still retain the possibility of passing on life indefinitely. The same thing is true among the higher animals. The cells of reproduction—the female ovum and the male sperm which fertilizes it —can together pass on life indefinitely. Thus, although the individual members of a species die, the species itself goes on living, often changing slowly, almost imperceptibly, as its many generations come and go.

CENTER: A new volvox colony is born before the outer part of the old one dies. BORDER: Twelve living things and their maximum life-expectancy in years.

6

20

50

100+

16

100

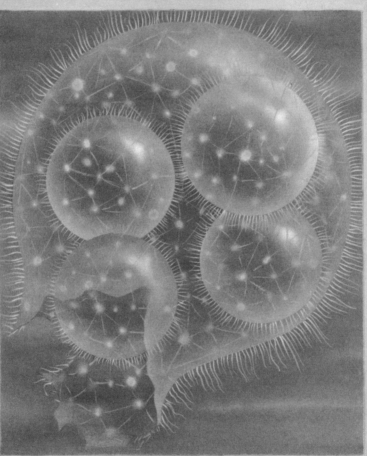

20+

150+

25

40

70

4000

Male and Female in Plants and Animals

Repeated several times on the opposite page are two symbols which you have doubtless seen on cages at the zoo. Zoologists and botanists use the circle with an arrow pointing upwards (the ancient sign for the planet Mars) to denote male. A circle with a cross pointing downwards (the ancient sign for the planet Venus) is used to denote female.

Even among plants which are relatively undeveloped we meet male and female cells. The two small pictures at the top center show, in diagram form, a thread of cells in a species of seaweed. Sometimes from one of these ordinary cells a specialist female reproduction cell develops. It blows itself up into a kind of tiny bud, shown in the right-hand picture, which pierces the outer membrane of the thread. Meanwhile, at another part of the same plant (left-hand picture) male cells are formed in groups of two. Equipped with tiny swimming whips, they move through the water and enter the hole that the bud has pierced. There they fertilize the female cell which then divides, producing the beginning of a new thread of cells.

The nut tree, shown in the remainder of the top strip, carries both male flowers (left) and female (right). There are a great many plants of this kind, and very often the pollen from the male flowers is carried to the female flowers by bees or other insects in search of nectar.

Many of the very large class of animals called invertebrates (animals without backbones) also carry both male and female cells in the same individual, as do the snails shown in our picture. But in the majority of more highly developed animals each individual is either distinctively male or distinctively female.

Animals are far freer to move about and wander away from one another than plants, and nature has devised many wonderful ways of making the male and female of the same species so attractive to each other that they are brought together to rear their young ones. In many cases this attraction lasts throughout a whole lifetime and male and female stay together, not only bringing young ones into the world but also feeding and tending them until they reach maturity.

It is not always easy to be sure just what it is that draws the male and female of a species together, but in many cases, at least, it seems to be the very marked differences between them. Among many birds, though not among all, the cocks have brilliantly colored feathers while the hens have a comparatively drab plumage. Among certain others, the song or cry of the hen is markedly different from that of the cock. The lion carries a large, flowing mane while the lioness is sleek and unmaned. Certain kinds of female fishes are very much larger than their male counterparts.

In certain cases the attraction between the sexes seems to be very simple and direct. One example is the glow-worm. The male is a winged insect which commonly flies about during the hours of darkness. The wingless female cannot join him in his flight, but as she crawls over the ground, some of the rings round her body give off a kind of phosphorescent light which guides him to her.

In many cases the attraction is more subtle. Among certain animals of prey it may be that the male is a better hunter than the female, and is a good provider for her young ones. Among certain birds it may be that both cock and hen have a different share in the tasks of nest-building, hatching eggs and feeding fledglings.

The whole story of the attraction of male and female of the same species is perhaps the greatest of all romances.

ABOVE: Two plants in which the individual is both male and female, as is the snail. BELOW: Two of the higher animals which show marked differences between the two sexes.

The Marvelous Skin —Protection and Sense Organ

What is a skin and what purpose does it serve?

First and foremost it is a protection, perhaps from heat, cold, drought or dampness, perhaps from attacks by other animals. But it may also serve as a sense organ, having a large number of different points especially sensitive to cold, pain, heat and pressure.

No single-celled creatures have a skin as we understand it, though in some the outer layer of protoplasm serves a similar purpose in a simple way. Frogs and other many-celled creatures, ourselves included, have skins made up of different sorts of cell, each designed to do a special job and all built up in layers.

If you look at a frog with the naked eye its skin appears to be a single layer. Yet seen through a microscope it is surprisingly complex. The diagram opposite shows that it consists of two main layers: the epidermis, or outer layer (1) and the corium, or inner layer (2).

Several layers of cells go to build up the epidermis. The topmost ones are dead. They make the tough outermost skin you can see with the naked eye. Beneath this dead layer, new cells are forever forming as replacements.

Below the epidermis lies the corium, a much thicker layer. Our own skins have the same two divisions. Layers of connective tissue make up most of this inner skin where veins and nerve-fibers thread their way in profusion. Our diagram shows veins and nerves in cross section, veins red (3) and nerves green (4). The frog's inner skin also contains pigment cells and glands (6). These end at the surface of the epidermis (5). The frog's glands produce a pungent liquid which is an effective weapon for such a defenseless creature. Glands of a similar kind in our own skins produce perspiration which, as it evaporates, helps to keep our bodies cool.

Though frogs have such complex skins, they are really thin-skinned animals and cannot stand the drying effects of hot sunshine. Thick-skinned lizards can sunbathe in safety but frogs spend most of their time in damp places.

Frogs replace their worn-out epidermis in a single operation, as if they were wriggling from a tight-fitting elastic coat. We change ours slowly but constantly—bit by bit in tiny scales which can scarcely be seen. Many animals never shed certain parts of their epidermis. Dead layers go on piling up until they project as horns, claws or hooves. The carapace of a tortoise looks more like armor than skin. Contrast the thickness of one of its "scales", shown by the brown and white block, with the thin green line which indicates the thickness of the frog's skin.

But it would be a mistake to imagine that the skin of every creature is the same thickness throughout. Some parts of your own skin are four times as thick as others. Where the body-surface gets most wear, the outer skin grows thickest. In most people these places are the heels, ankles and neck. Heavy manual workers, of course, may also get toughened hands.

The color of people's skins varies widely in different parts of the world. We regard some Orientals as "yellow-skinned", certain Africans as "black" and most peoples of the western hemisphere as "white". These terms really refer to the colors of the pigment cells of the inner skin. The "white" peoples possess few yellow or red pigment cells; Mongols, Eskimos and Red Indians have far more. In Africans and Melanesians, yellow and brown cells outumber the rest.

Pigmentation affords protection against the sun's rays. The longer we sit in the sun, the more our pigment cells increase. Peoples living for countless generations in various climates evolve different pigmentation patterns.

TOP LEFT: A frog and cross-sections of its skin. CENTER: A giant tortoise and cross-sections of its shell. RIGHT: Relative thickness of human skin at arrowed points. BELOW LEFT: Pigment cells before and after sunburn. RIGHT: Pigment cells in white, yellow, and brown-skinned populations.

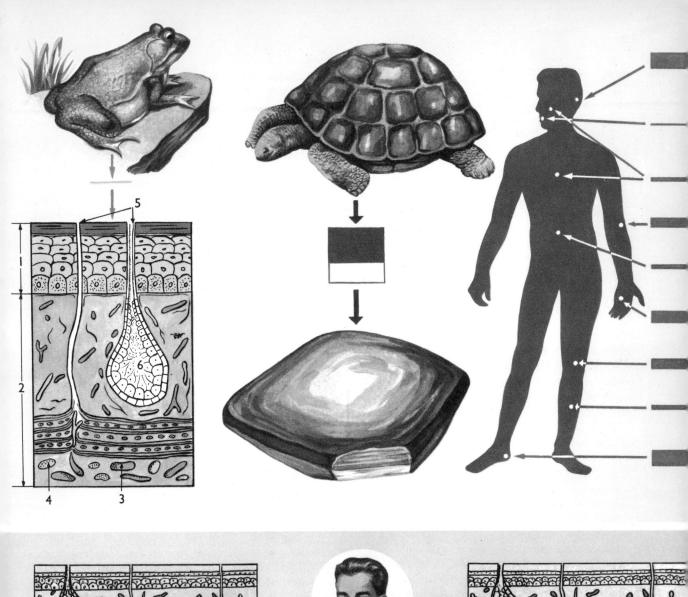

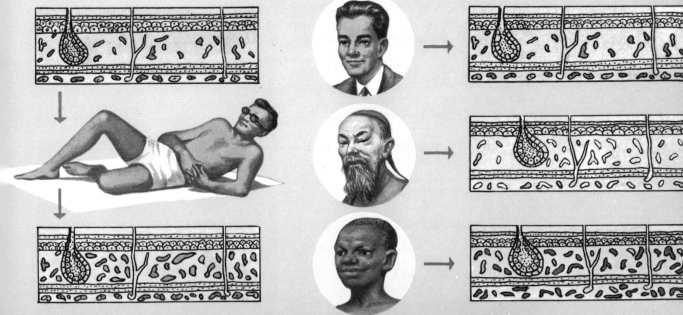

Tissues for Padding, Tissues for Power

We have seen that the skin is very complicated. Nevertheless, perhaps we may think of it for a moment as a kind of wrapping around an even more complicated parcel. If we ask ourselves what are the main things this parcel contains we shall probably think first of the hard, bony skeleton which gives the parcel its distinctive shape, and next of the many highly complex and delicate "machines", all geared to work closely together, such as the heart, the liver, the kidneys and various digestive organs. We may also think of the wonderful supply system—the bloodstream —and of the controls—the nervous system. But there is another very important item: the tissues which serve, among other things, as padding and support for all these vital contents.

These are the connective tissues. If you could see them apart from the rest of the body, you would see how they provide a kind of ghostly framework which supports and protects many items, ranging from the heart to the minutest nerves and blood vessels. Certain simple animals, such as the jellyfish, are made up almost entirely of tissues of this sort.

The cells of the skin, as we saw, are tightly packed, but the cells of connective tissues are widely spaced. One of their tasks is to build up the fibers which support the various organs of the body. Another is to provide a reserve supply of energy-producing food: fat. Carried along by the bloodstream, particles of fat gather inside the connective-tissue cells. In time they swell the cell walls. Groups of fat-filled cells grow bunched like grapes.

Human beings store up most of their fat in layers just beneath the skin. The biggest storehouse is under the skin which lines the abdomen. Certain other backboned animals store fat elsewhere. Camels, for instance, draw on their fat-filled humps for energy during long desert treks where food is scarce.

Body tissues are adapted to fulfill several functions. Connective tissues can build up to form the tougher networks of fiber which we call sinews and tendons. These serve to link muscles to bones. Muscle itself is tissue: the tissue which makes possible our every movement. Hundreds of red muscle pistons drive the machine that is our body. The illustrations on the facing page give some idea of their intricate arrangement and the way they work.

Like all other body tissues, muscles are made up of specially designed cells. Many cells, surrounded by a membrane, form a single bundle of muscle-fiber. Several bundles go to make up each muscle.

There are special sorts of muscle to work the heart and the intestines, and other sorts to effect the movement of the limbs. Those which work the heart and digestive organs are *involuntary* muscles: we cannot normally control their workings by any act of will. If we swallow a piece of food we lose control of it the moment it passes beyond the mouth. The smooth muscle of the gullet has taken over. Contracting behind the food, relaxing before it, it ensures the first stage of digestion by remote control.

Contracting and relaxing is the special work of muscles. Our pictures of a human arm show how its muscles do their job. These are *voluntary* muscles—muscles which we can control by our own choice. They are also called striated, or furrowed, muscles because of the strip-like pattern which the muscle-bundles make. At rest, a muscle-bundle is long and thin. Contracted, as it is when you grip an object in your hand, the muscle grows much shorter and much thicker. The shortening of muscles, attached to bones by means of tendons, pulls the jointed bones which act as levers, enabling us to move about.

To make these muscles move just as and when we want them to, there must be some system of sending them messages to which they will respond. This is one of the important tasks undertaken by the nervous system.

LEFT: Man's muscle system. RIGHT: Arm muscles relaxed (top three pictures) and contracted.

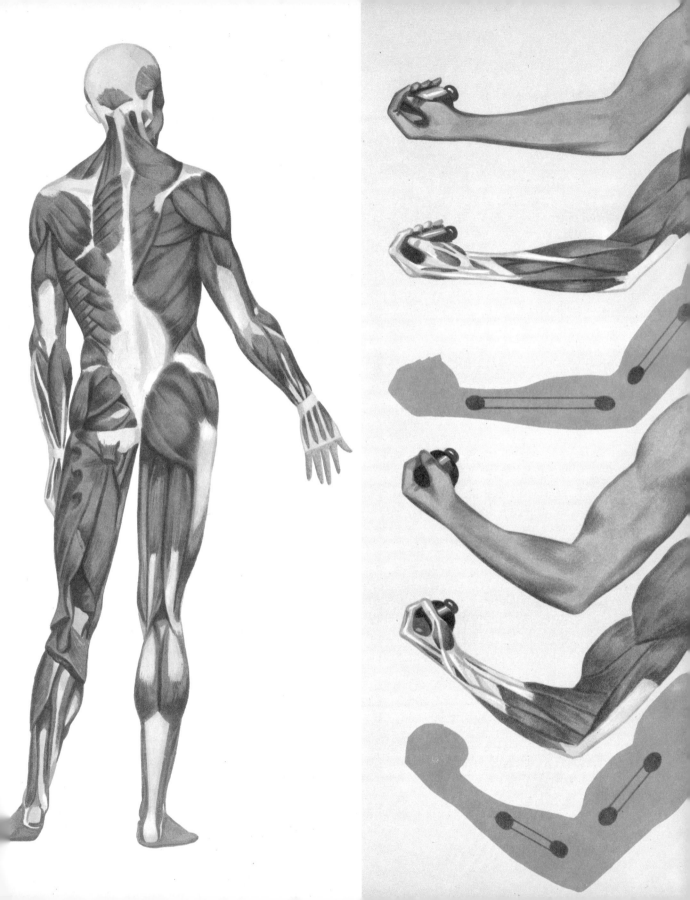

How We Keep in Touch

If you burn your finger with a match it is not the finger itself which registers the sense of pain. Nerve-ends in the finger flash an impulse—rather like an electric impulse in a telephone wire—through a maze of unbroken nerve "cables", each made up of bundles of "wires" or fibers, to an "exchange" housed in your spinal column. Only when the impulse gets there do you cry "Oh!" An "automatic operator" instantly interprets the message and flashes back a new one along a separate, outgoing nerve line, a motor nerve which tells your finger muscles to pull away from the burning flame. It is thus that nerves keep us in touch with the outside world.

Our own nervous system is not unique. Many quite simple, literally brainless, creatures have a nervous system which helps to keep them alive by enabling them to recognize the difference between foe and food or fight and flight. The freshwater hydra pictured on page 101, is a good example. Even the single-celled ameba, which has no true nervous system, is yet able to react to certain stimuli such as light and possibly, also, pain. Worms have their nerve network centered in a primitively developed brain that runs the length of the body.

When we pull a finger away from a burning match we make an unthinking or involuntary movement, controlled by local centers in a nervous system not unlike a worm's. But human beings also make voluntary movements, controlled by a thinking brain — movements of a kind impossible for a worm to make.

Our brain seems to be a group of outgrowths from a spinal cord. It probably evolved, over an immense period, from simple brains like that of the woodlouse pictured opposite. The pith-like cord which runs the length of the creature's body is shown yellow and its brain blue. The other illustrations (left) show that the human brain is bigger than that of any of the other creatures shown in relation to its overall size. Size, however, is not as important as complexity of brain.

The human brain is not one but several outgrowths, all fulfilling different organizing functions but all housed under a single roof, the skull. Under the back of the brain is the part known as the cerebellum. This helps to regulate the way we move. With only half a cerebellum we could not even walk straight.

The upper main part of the brain, the cerebrum, makes up nine-tenths of its total bulk. Its outer layer, or cortex, has a grey, rubbery, wrinkled surface unlike the smooth cortex of the lower animals. In general the more wrinkled a creature's cortex, the more intelligent it seems to be. Scientists tell us that the cerebrum is responsible for those processes which in everyday language we call reasoning, feeling and will. Parts of it also control our actions.

The cerebrum is made up of two hemispheres. The left one affects muscle movements on the right side of the body, while the right one affects the movements on the left side. In healthy people, nerve messages travel as they do because the brain's nerve fibers cross each other in an oblong organ situated where the brain joins the spine. Its name, the medulla oblongata, comes from the Latin words *medulla,* meaning the marrow in the middle, and *oblongus,* meaning oblong.

Our illustration compares the thinking brain with a submarine commander. The eye (periscope) sends its message to the brain (the commander) whose judgment controls the movements of the limbs (the sailors).

If you burn your finger on a match you do not have to *think* what to do. But if you meet an angry bull in a field midway between two gates you must make a snap decision. In such a tight spot your brain works at an incredible speed. And when you decide which way to run, nerve-impulses from brain to leg muscles move at almost 300 m.p.h. Even the commander of the most modern submarine could not change course half as quickly as you begin to run.

LEFT: Animals and their brains. TOP RIGHT: Woodlouse, showing nerve cord (yellow) and brain (blue). BOTTOM RIGHT: Controls of movement in man and in submarine.

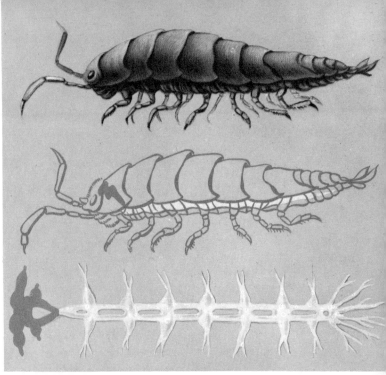

Growth and Tissues in Flower and Tree

We have already caught a glimpse of the great variety of animal cell-structures which have evolved from simple single-cell creatures. Plant cell-structures have also undergone a marvelous process of change and specialization. We see something of its results when we contrast the towering trunk of a giant California redwood with the microscopic algae which turn summer pond-water green. Despite the vast difference in their size, they have more in common with each other than either of them has with any animal.

A comparison between plant and animal tissues shows why. Animals have muscle tissues which make movement possible, and nerve tissues which co-ordinate and control various movements. Plants have neither nerves nor muscles, since they need not move to find their food. Green plants simply manufacture it from substances in the earth and in the air, with the help of energy provided by sunlight.

Looking at a young baby you could make a reasonable guess about how big it will eventually grow. But looking at an oak seedling who could say what size and shape the mature tree will be? In mature animals, cells no longer multiply fast enough to keep the body growing. They multiply only fast enough to keep pace with the loss of old cells as these wear out. But plants never stop growing. Whatever their age there will always be cells somewhere multiplying fast enough to push out new leaves, twigs or even branches. Indeed a plant like a bramble is always throwing out fresh runners. Given time, a single blackberry bush could colonize a whole continent.

Plants lack the beauty of movement which characterizes animals, but they make up for it in the amazing colors and patterns of their flowers and leaves. The beauty of flower and foliage which we admire is made up of countless cells arranged in innumerable patterns, fulfilling roles as wonderful as animal cells.

With the help of the microscope we can examine some of the specialized cells which build up the different parts of a plant. Our top illustrations compare cross-sections through the stem of a viola (left) and the leaf of a yellow iris (right). These magnified cell patterns differ not merely because they come from different plants but also because each does a different job of work. Leaf tissues are adapted to serve as the "lungs" of a green plant; root tissues act as pumps to draw up nourishment from the soil; stem tissues form a canal, joining roots and leaves and providing a passage for food between them.

We have noticed that there are thick-skinned and thin-skinned animals. The same is true of plants. Like animals they develop an outer layer of dead cells. In a sense the bark of a tree is like an epidermis. It may be thin as in ash trees, or inches thick as in the giant redwoods. Plants also grow a kind of epidermis from the inside. For example, each summer oak trees make new growth. Each winter they rest. If you look at a tree stump you will see the result.

In summer new cells form just under the bark, pushing it out to make a thicker trunk. But last year's cells slowly begin wrinkling and hardening into a tough wood ring. So we get the pattern you see in the cross-section through an oak stump.

Counting tree-rings is an accurate way of telling a tree's age. There is a true story about a brown ash, 100 feet high and 17 feet thick. People guessed it to be nearly five centuries old. When they chopped it down and counted its rings they found it was only a third of that age.

Today, scientists have a special name for the study of tree-rings: dendochronology, which merely means tree time-estimating. They find that tree-rings vary in thickness. The better a growing season, the thicker the rings. With this knowledge they can match up rings in trees long dead and map out a climate chart for many centuries past.

TOP LEFT: Viola and magnified cross-section through its stem. TOP RIGHT: Yellow iris and magnified section through a leaf. BELOW: Cutting down a tree reveals its annual growth-rings.

Scales and Hair, Fur and Feathers

We have noticed that the skin acts as a protector against heat and cold. This is perhaps less important to reptiles, whose blood changes temperature with their surroundings, than to birds and mammals, which keep warm in all weathers. Here fur and feathers play their part. They trap a warm layer of air between the skin surface and the air outside.

A bird's feathers help to keep it warm. They also help it to fly. How did it come to possess such a useful covering?

To find the answer we must first look at fishes and reptiles, both of which lived long before the first birds. As a protective body covering many species evolved scales: downward growths from the outer skin. Rooted in the inner skin, angled to lie flat, and sloping backward in streamline fashion, these form a fine chain-mail covering. You can see this in our picture of a present-day fish. Each overlapping scale adds growth to its outer edges, forming a pattern which reminds us of the growth rings in a tree-stump.

Some prehistoric land reptiles leaped along the ground or from tree to tree. In time each of their scales split into several strips, thus producing more air resistance and aiding flight. In the course of millions of years these scales became feathers, and their wearers birds. Thus even a peacock's tail owes its origin to simple scales. A magnified bit of feather shows how hard scale has become soft feather. What remains a solid plate in fishes has in birds become a main stem with finer shafts sprouting alternately from either side. From these side shafts sprout others, finer still.

When a feather first appears above the skin a tiny capsule encloses it. This falls away and leaves the feather free to spread out. Feathers go on growing because they are fed by multiplying cells deep in the skin. They meet with considerable wear and tear and soon become torn and jaded.

But birds renew them by a yearly or, more frequently, by a twice-yearly molt.

Not all birds have the same number of feathers. For instance, kingfishers have around 1,000, swans about 25,000. Nor are feathers equally dense all over a bird's body. Only a few great flight feathers cover a swan's wings. Twenty thousand of its feathers are on its neck.

Just as feathers are adapted to the different needs of different birds, so hair varies with mammals. A rhino's "horn", a porcupine's quills, a rabbit's fur, are all forms of hair. Man's prehistoric ancestors probably had an all-over covering of hair. When they felt cold their skins doubtless contracted, raising the hairs to trap warm air. Our skins still contract when we are cold, but our "gooseflesh" no longer serves the same purpose.

Human hairs grow in hollows, or follicles, which dip deep down inside the inner skin. Our illustration shows one magnified. Linked with each follicle, oil-filled glands (shown yellow) lubricate the surface skin and help to keep it supple. Each hair grows as the soft cells multiply at its root and push up the ones above. Above the skin a hair is made chiefly of dead, scale-like cells which make it shine. We grow new hairs to replace old ones roughly every four or five months. On an average person they grow at the rate of about three-quarters of an inch per month.

Hair color depends on pigment cells inside the hairs. Blondes tend to have finer hairs and more of them than red-heads. Our illustrations show the average number of hairs per head for blonde, brunette, black-haired and red-headed people, and the relative thickness of a hair from each.

Not all hairs are round. Some are oval and give rise to wavy hair. Hairdressers artificially make round hairs oval to create a "permanent" wave. But it is only permanent until new, round hairs grow to replace the oval ones.

ABOVE: Peacock and magnified piece of its tail feather. CENTER: Magnified section through a human hair. RIGHT: Hair-densities of blonde, brunette, black-haired and red-headed people. BELOW: Scaled animals and magnified fish scale.

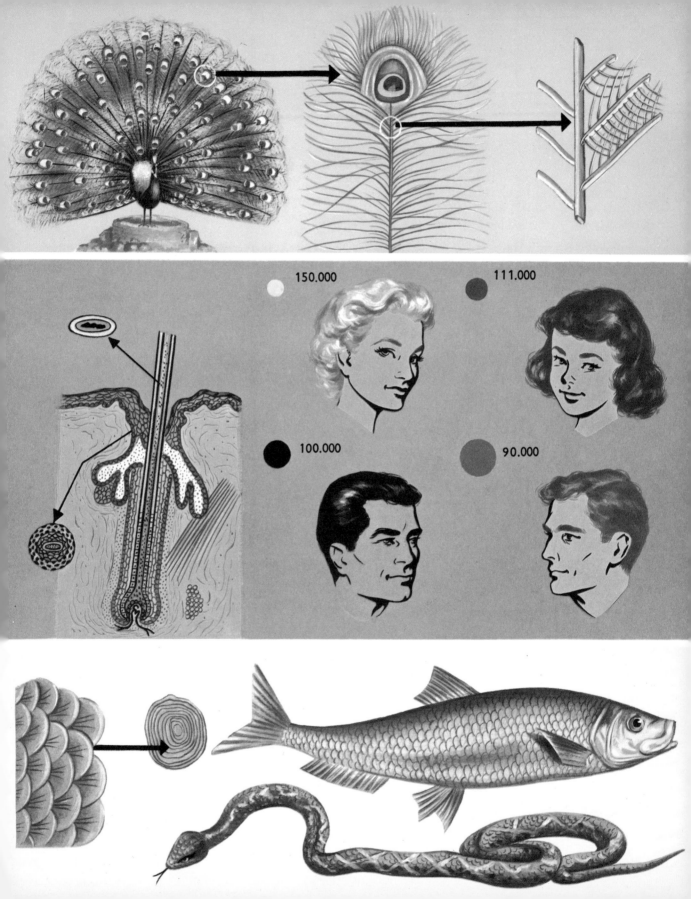

150.000

111.000

100.000

90.000

Animal Armor, Animal Framework

By far the hardest and most durable parts of the bodies of human beings and most other mammals are the bones, which often survive intact many centuries after all trace of flesh has disappeared.

Most living creatures have some sort of skeleton but not all of them carry it inside their bodies as we do. Although the word skeleton usually brings to mind the bony internal framework of an animal's body, there is a quite different kind of skeleton which, in many animals, serves as a sort of outer support and armor. The glass-like outer skeleton in our first illustration belongs to a tiny sea organism called a radiolarian. Its lovely pattern of holes plays a vital part in the creature's daily life. Snug inside its external shell, the radiolarian sticks pseudopodia, or false feet, through these holes in all directions to help it to move about and find food.

Many different kinds of creatures have external skeletons, wonderfully adapted to their way of life. Snail shells are an obvious example. So is the outside skeleton of the beetle, made of a substance called chitin (from a Greek word *chiton*, meaning tunic). This wonderful skeleton is strong enough to give protection, yet light enough to let the beetle fly.

Unlike flying insects, crayfish and lobsters have no need to worry about the weight they carry, since they live under water and are buoyed up by it. But they do need a sturdy coat of mail to protect their tasty flesh from other hungry sea-dwellers. A heavy suit of mail, made of chitin heavily reinforced with hard chalk, and jointed to make movement easy, is ideal for their purpose.

You could liken external skeletons to the solid mud domes of primitive houses. You could compare internal skeletons with the steel framework of a modern office building. All backboned animals are built around a framework of that kind: frogs, lizards, fishes, birds and man himself. True, there are many differences between the skeletons of all these creatures. Man's well developed lungs, for instance, are protected by a strong container of ribs, all joined to the spine and most of them also connected to the breastbone by cartilage; but the frog, which can breathe through its skin and is less dependent on its specialized breathing organ, has no true ribs and only an insignificant breastbone. Yet despite all differences of this kind, all backboned animals have certain important features in common. They all have a skull and a flexible spine made up of many separate bones, and all those which spend part or all of their time on land have four limbs.

Human bones are beautifully planned to do their job. Engineers have found that hollow steel tubes can carry almost as great a weight as solid steel pillars of the same diameter. Our hollow bones, constructed on the same principle, give us a framework which is at once light and enormously strong. Nature uses this same powerful hollow-stem design in bamboo, wheat, reeds, grasses and many other plants.

The adult human skeleton, made up of 206 separate light-weight bones, weighs only about 22 pounds. Many of these bones, skilfully jointed and hitched by tendons and cartilage to muscles, give our bodies a freedom and variety of movement unrivalled by the most complex of modern machines.

At one time people thought that bone was a lifeless structure. Now, scientists have shown how living connective tissue cells build up bone with the help of calcium and vitamin D. Milk is a good source of calcium, while summer sunshine helps us to build up a supply of vitamin D. Both are essential, especially to children, whose bones are still in the formative stage.

ABOVE: External skeletons of radiolarian (left), lobster (top) and wasp (bottom). Protective plates resemble parts of armor. BELOW: Internal skeletons of frog, fish, lizard, goose and man.

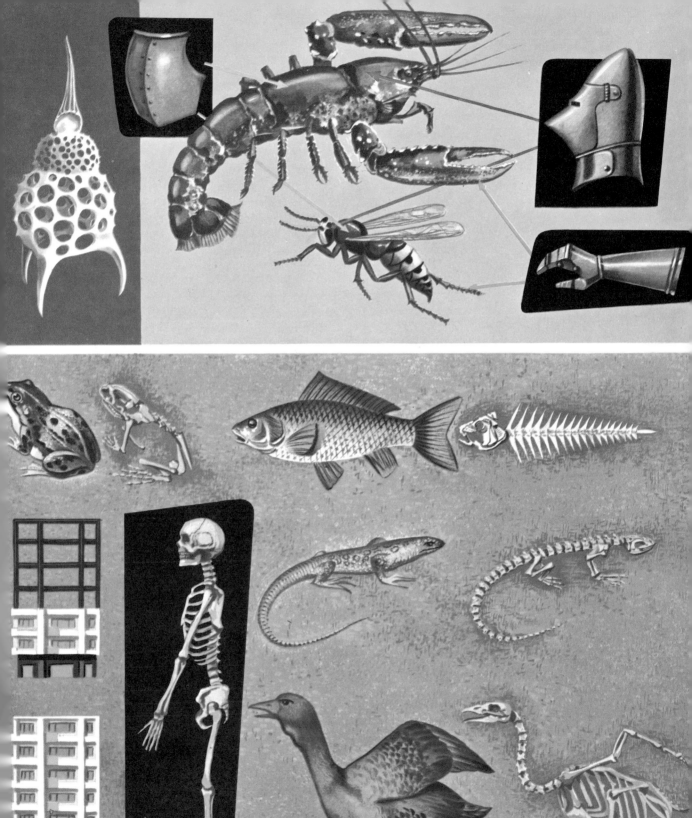

Inventions by Nature and Man

All animals and some simple plants can move about in search of food or materials for making food and to escape from enemies. The means of moving about which nature has invented are many and fascinating.

We have already seen something of the simplest kinds of animal movement — the flow of protoplasm in various single-cell creatures and the pushing out of false feet in others. The white cells of our own blood wander through our bloodstream with the help of false feet. They are like some great anti-disease army, forever patrolling the body in search of harmful bacteria, which they engulf as an ameba engulfs its food.

Still stranger are the movements of diatoms, minute sea plants related to freshwater algae. Beneath a microscope they look just like some splendid jewel of incredibly precise workmanship. Each consists of a two-part, silica-coated cell-wall. The parts fit into one another like a pill-box and its lid. To move about, these fantastic little plants set up a flow of granular protoplasm along a groove around their outer surface. Passing out of the "lid" through a narrow crack, the protoplasm flows round the organism and re-enters by another opening opposite the first. Our illustration gives an idea how this works, like the rotation of the caterpillar tracks of a tank.

Many other single-cell water creatures propel themselves by means of tiny swimming lashes or whips. Their rhythmic beating of the water reminds us of the teams of oars which rowed the Viking ships of old.

Most animals with which we are familiar move neither by simple protoplasmic flow nor by swimming but by contracting and relaxing muscles. We are apt to connect muscles mainly with **large,** powerful animals, but in fact the humble earthworm moves about by means of muscles. We have all seen them sliding along the ground, but few of us can claim to know just how they move.

They do so with the help of two sorts of muscles which make up the outer wall of the body. Circular muscle fibers surround the body like hoops. Long muscles run along its length. These two sets of muscles work alternately. When a worm contracts its circular muscles it grows long and thin. When it contracts its long muscles it becomes short and fat. If both sets of muscles acted simultaneously the worm would get nowhere. Watch one moving and you will see that the muscular contraction starts at one end and ripples down most of the worm's length like a wave. This peristaltic movement — its name comes from Greek words meaning wrapped around — is as vital to man as it is to the earthworm. It is that kind of movement which keeps food moving in our intestines, and is carried on by muscles which we cannot consciously control.

Man's own body movements were naturally developed but he has himself invented new ways of moving farther and faster than his own limited muscle-power can take him. One of man's greatest recent triumphs of invention is the jet.

Yet propulsion by reaction, the method of movement which jets employ, existed long before men knew what it was. The first time a man ever dived from a boat, the boat was pushed backwards by reaction as he thrust himself forward, into the water.

Millions of years before men even existed, certain animals moved by jet propulsion. Our picture shows the squid, one of nature's "living fossils". Although it can move by means of its tentacles, it can also suck in water and squirt it out forcibly to drive itself rapidly through the ocean depths. Even the dragonfly larvae found in ditches or ponds propel themselves by means of water jets.

No doubt man was the first creature to *think* of tanks, oars, jets and rockets, but diatoms, various single-cell animals and squids made use of them **long, long before he did so.**

The diatom moves like a tank, certain single-cell animals like a Viking ship, the squid like a rocket or a jet plane. A worm moves by muscles like those of our intestines, as they pass our food along.

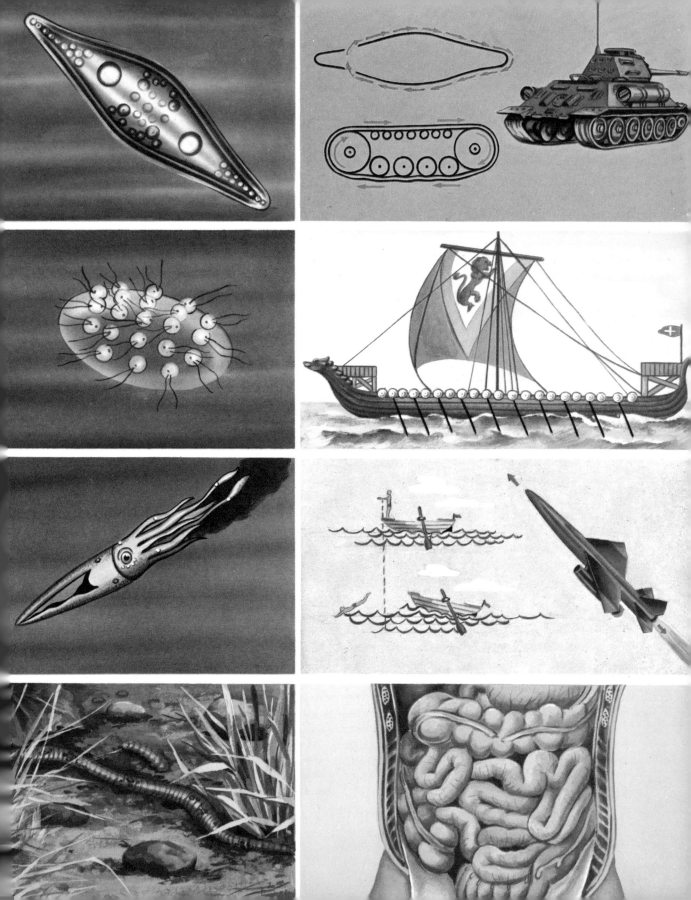

Fins, Limbs and Wings

Many millions of years ago there were no land animals, only sea creatures, adapted to moving under water. Far heavier and denser than air, water can support the weight of huge animals, including giant whales whose body organs would be crushed by their own weight out of water. In many ways its high density makes water an easier medium to move through than air.

To help them move through the waters many fishes have evolved shapes more highly streamlined than any submarine. If you watch a fish swimming you will notice that it does not propel itself by means of its fins, as many of us imagine. It holds its pectoral fins — one behind each gill plate — flat against its sides to increase the streamlining of its body. Muscles on either side of its backbone alternately contract and relax, moving the tail from side to side. While the tail is moving from either side towards the middle it is spread out, and presses backwards against the water to push the fish forward. When moving from the middle towards either side it closes, and simply slips through the water.

Not all fishes swim by moving their bodies and tails from side to side. Flatfish, skates and rays swim by undulating up and down. Eels also swim by body undulations, and so do snakes, though the latter have no fins at all. In most cases a fish's fins act as stabilizers rather than as a means of getting about.

Yet some fish do use pectoral fins to help them move. The strange climbing perch and mud-skippers of tropical regions can move about on fins over land as well as through water. It was probably from creatures of this kind that land animals gradually evolved — first amphibians, then reptiles, then warm blooded birds and mammals. All these different kinds of animals slowly developed organs of movement suited to their own surroundings. Yet experts can still trace a bird's wings and clawed feet, as well as human arms and legs, to fishes' fins from which they evolved.

Even man, who is essentially a land animal, can thrust himself unaided through water. But he cannot fly unaided through the air. Only in very recent years has he learned to make machines to rival the flying ability of birds. *Their* adaptations to the demands of air travel have taken place over millions of years.

Although birds, like airplanes, are lightly built — their bones are very light and hollow — they are still "heavier-than-air machines". A bird shot while on the wing plummets to earth like a stone. It is only their cunningly fashioned wings, controlled by powerful muscles, that enable them to overcome the force of gravity. As the wings move upward and backward the feathers are closed and slip easily through the air. As they move downward once more, the feathers spread out, thrusting hard against the air and pushing the bird forward. Furthermore, the bird's body is streamlined like the wing of a plane. The upper part of its body has a larger surface area than the lower part. So air flowing over the whole of the bird becomes compressed underneath and rarefied above. This helps to give an upward lift.

Not all birds fly by wing-beats. Gulls and albatrosses can stay airborne for some time by skilfully angling their stationary, widespread wings to catch updrafts of air.

Birds like the lark, with weaker, shorter wings, contrive to stay aloft by rapid wing-beats. Larks have such skilful flight control that they can remain in one spot for several seconds, as if suspended by an invisible cord. The kestrel combines gliding flight with rapid wing-beats. It can pause in mid-air, suspended like a lark, while it surveys the earth below, seeking mice and other small animals upon which it preys.

TOP: Three birds — lark, gull and kestrel — and their typical patterns of flight. BOTTOM: Three different fishes, and how each of them moves through the water.

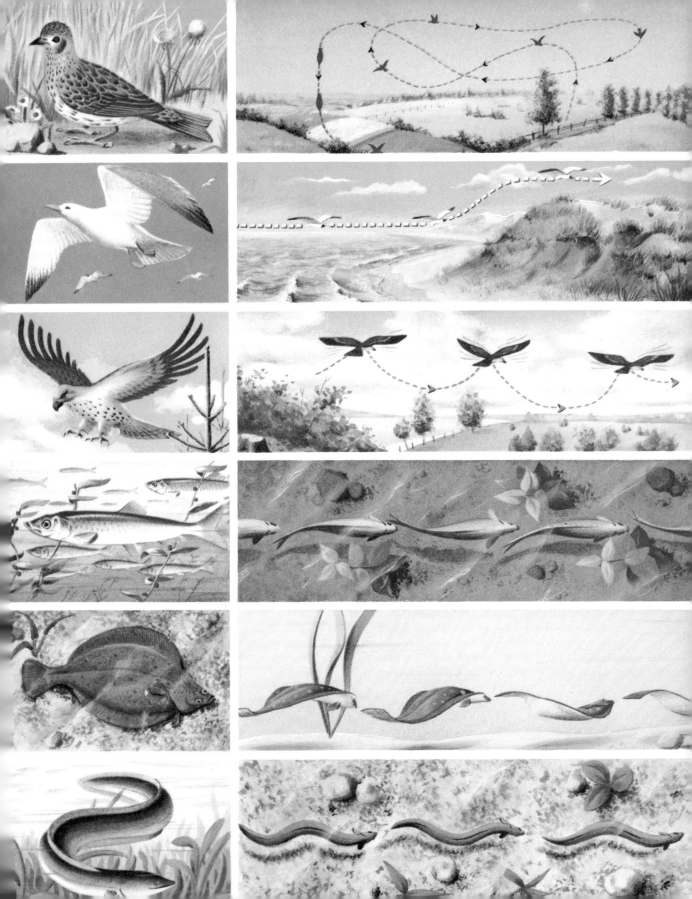

Different Mouths for Different Diets

Few animals could live long without moving. They must move to find food. And they must eat to live. Indeed, many creatures almost seem to live to eat. Like man before he learned to farm and thus control his food supply, they find life one long struggle for food.

Most plants make food from materials in the soil and the air. They are living chemical factories. But almost every animal must live at the expense of plants or other animals. Even the one-celled ameba feeds on microscopic plants. Bigger organisms prey on the amebae. Small fish eat those organisms. Big fish eat the small ones. So the great food snowball grows.

Why is eating so important? Just as gasoline fuels a car, so food fuels our bodies. Every movement we make uses up some energy. Food replaces it. But we cannot utilize food until we have broken it down into a form which the body can absorb.

The breaking-down process starts inside the mouth. Incisor teeth (outlined pink in the picture opposite) act rather like scissors, to cut up food. Canines (blue) crush it, as if with hammer blows. Molars (green) grind it between their hard, flat surfaces. The rough-surfaced tongue (outlined yellow) acts like rollers, mortar and pestle, breaking down the food into even smaller fragments. Special glands (colored mauve) cover the food with saliva, helping to reduce it to a pulp. The food then slides down the gullet to undergo still further transformation.

Man is omnivorous: he eats both flesh and vegetable foods. However all mammals do not do so. Those which live only on vegetable foods are called herbivorous animals, while meat-eaters are called carnivorous. Often you can tell what food a creature eats by looking at its mouth.

The flesh-eating tiger has long, strong canine teeth for tearing the meat. Its incisors, for cutting, are small. But its upper jaw is wider than the lower one. As the two move together the powerful molars do not grind like ours, but interlock to slice up the food.

The grass-eating cow has many flat-crowned molars which grind grass to pulp. Unlike the tiger's upper jaw with its well-developed canine teeth, a cow's upper jaw has neither canines nor incisors. But in the lower jaw it has both, near the front of the mouth and pointing forward. Together with the tongue they enable the cow to tear up the grass as it grazes in the meadow.

The pig eats both vegetable and animal foods, as we do. Its skull shows that it combines some of the features of both the cow and the tiger. Its forward-sloping incisors near the front of the mouth help it to tear up growing vegetation; its powerful molars can deal with animal food.

Not all animals can masticate their food. Many fishes as well as frogs and reptiles, catch their prey and swallow it whole. Their digestive organs must do the work of teeth. Birds, too, are toothless. "Grindstones" accumulated in their crop do the work of cutting and grinding food. Some birds have beaks which serve as spears, others have beaks strong enough to crack a hard-shelled nut, and the pelican's beak actually serves as a larder.

Like mammals' teeth, birds' beaks often betray the kind of food they eat. Four examples are shown opposite. The slender, pointed bill reveals an insect-eater; the strong, stubby beak a bird that lives on seeds. The hooked beaks of birds of prey remind us of a tiger's jaws. The long pointed bills of storks and herons act as spears to help them to catch fish.

Many beaks and many teeth are specially adapted to capture prey. Beakless, toothless creatures have evolved other weapons of attack and capture. A spider's glands enable it to spin a web to trap flies. The ant-lion digs a hole in the sand, hides in it, and then leaps out and seizes any unsuspecting ant that passes by.

TOP: Functions of different parts of the mouth explained by a color key. SECOND: Structures of three mouths which devour different diets. THIRD: Different beaks for different foods. FOURTH: Capturing food with neither teeth nor beak.

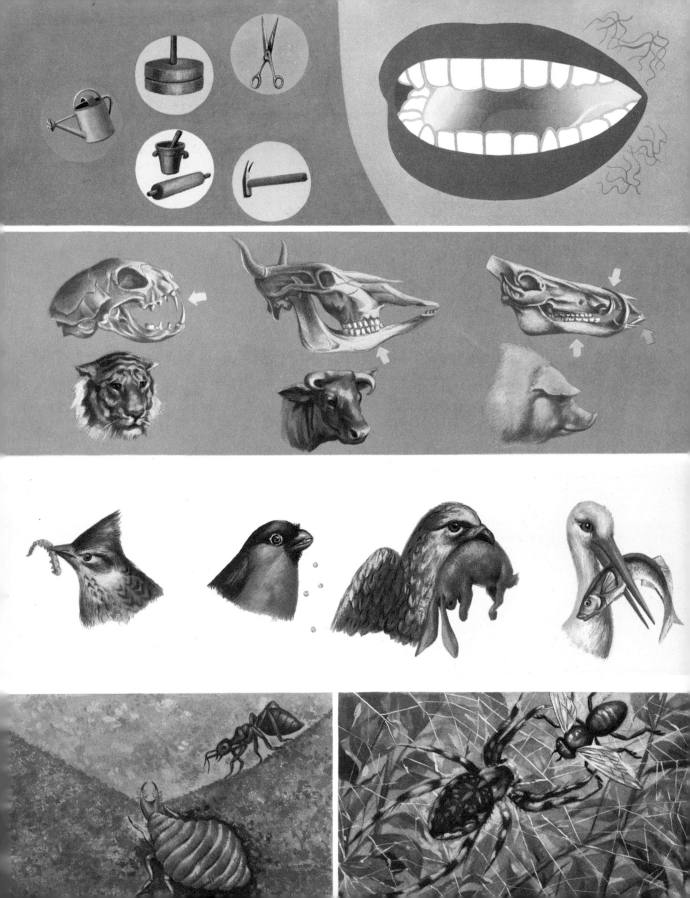

Gas used as a Solid,
A Solid used as Gas

We have seen that different kinds of animals eat many different kinds of food. Yet all these foodstuffs are made up of the same few chemical elements. Carbohydrates and fats consist of carbon, hydrogen and oxygen combined in various proportions. Proteins include all these three elements and also nitrogen.

Carbohydrates, which include starch and sugar, are the "quick-burning" fuel foods. They react readily with the oxygen we breathe and provide us with warmth and energy quite soon after we have eaten them. Fats digest more slowly and provide energy for later on. Proteins are the foods which build up the bodies of growing young people and repair the worn-out body tissues of all of us. The name protein comes from a Greek word meaning "I am first" and proteins do, indeed, come first in the building up and repair of our bodies.

All the four main chemical elements which go to make up food are extremely abundant throughout the earth. Hydrogen accounts for two out of every three atoms in the water of all the earth's oceans and rivers, while oxygen accounts for the third. Oxygen also accounts for about a fifth of all the gases in the air. Carbon forms a very considerable part of almost every living thing, as well as of coal, charcoal, chalk, limestone and mineral oils. Nitrogen accounts for close to four-fifths of the gases in the earth's atmosphere.

Two of these elements — nitrogen and carbon — provide a particularly interesting part of the story of living things. Nitrogen is a colorless gas, yet it plays little part in the business of life except when it is combined with other elements to form solid substances. Carbon is a black, solid substance, yet it circulates from animals to plants only when it is combined with oxygen to form carbon dioxide gas.

The top picture deals with the way in which nitrogen circulates. Through their roots, plants take in salts containing nitrogen. Inside the plant this nitrogen combines with carbon, oxygen and hydrogen to produce protein foods. Some animals eat the protein foods of plants which help to build new kinds of proteins in their own bodies. Other animals eat flesh, milk or eggs and so make use of these new proteins. Animal droppings and the buried remains of dead animals provide the soil with various solid substances which contain nitrogen. Certain kinds of bacteria in the soil break down these substances once more into salts containing nitrogen which plants can absorb.

In that part of the nitrogen story (and it is the larger part), nitrogen moves from soil to plant, plant to animal, animal to soil, and soil to plant once more entirely as part of solid substances. But there is another part of the story in which nitrogen in the form of gas appears. The roots of some plants, such as beans, peas, clover and lupines, contain little swellings which are the homes of bacteria. These bacteria can take gaseous nitrogen from the air and combine it with other things to form nitrates which plants can use.

The bottom picture deals with the way in which carbon circulates. Plants take carbon dioxide gas from the air in order to build up food. Animals and men eat the food. In their bodies, the carbon in the food combines with the oxygen they breathe to form carbon dioxide gas. They breathe this out into the air, and plants can again make use of it.

Whenever we burn coal or mineral oil we are in fact burning the remains of plants or tiny animal organisms that lived a great age ago. All of them contained carbon. When they burn, they combine with oxygen to form carbon dioxide, giving another source of supply to living plants. The plants take in the carbon dioxide, which could be harmful to animals if there were too much of it in the air, and give out oxygen which animals need to breathe.

TOP: How nitrogen, a gas, passes from soil to plant to animal and back to soil mainly as an ingredient of solid substances. BOTTOM: How carbon, a solid, combines with oxygen in breathing and burning and reaches plants as carbon dioxide gas.

Turning Food into Warmth and Energy, Bone and Muscle

In normal circumstances the first concern of every living organism is to preserve its own life. Thus making or finding, eating and digesting food is perhaps the main life's work of every living thing. Only green plants can manufacture their own food supply from non-living materials. All animals and all plants such as fungi, which contain no green chlorophyll, must depend on vegetable matter or on flesh which, if we trace it back far enough, was ultimately built up from vegetable foodstuffs.

Every animal, when it has found its food, must be able to convert it into fuel for warmth and energy and also into part and parcel of the very substances of its own body: flesh, blood, bone and muscle. An important part — though by no means the whole — of this elaborate process, which we call metabolism, goes on in the stomach. And it is extraordinary what a tremendously wide variety of different stomachs nature has evolved, all adapted to the different diets and different surroundings of their possessors.

On the lowest rung of the ladder of life, many single-cell creatures, like the ameba we saw on page 17, can use almost every part of their tiny bodies to serve as a kind of temporary stomach. Larger soft-bodied animals often have permanent stomachs which are little more than simple sacs for containing and absorbing food, while in many fishes, birds and mammals the stomach is a highly complicated and specialized organ, forming only part of an even more complex digestive system.

Among certain deep-sea fishes whose opportunities for finding food may be somewhat rare, the stomach is extraordinarily large compared with the rest of the body. Apart from its large jaws and its long whip-like tail, the strange fish shown at the top left of the opposite page seems to be almost all stomach. The other fish pictured has a stomach similar to a loose plastic bag. When it swallows a victim almost as big as itself this "bag" stretches until it becomes semi-transparent like the walls of a tightly-blown toy balloon. The teeth of both these fishes are used only to seize the prey. They cannot cut it up, so it must be swallowed whole.

Birds have no teeth at all, and although few of them swallow such prodigious morsels as many deep-sea fishes do, their stomachs must still do the work of cutting and grinding food which most mammals do with their teeth. Part of the bird's stomach, made up of powerful muscle-tissue with a hard leathery surface-covering, is well equipped to cope with this job. Pieces of grit and small stones which the bird swallows also play a part in grinding the food.

The cross-section through a lobster's stomach (right center) almost suggests that the lobster has swallowed its teeth. The grey patches near the masticating plate (shown brown) are covered with rows of fine saw-like teeth.

An animal which chews the cud has a stomach made up of several compartments, though part of it is only a modified form of gullet and produces no digestive juices. A cow's food passes first into the largest compartment (A), where multitudes of single-cell organisms help to break down the hard cellulose cell-walls of the grass. It then travels to the second compartment (B) which carries the process of digestion a stage further before returning the food to the cow's mouth for "cud-chewing". Eventually the food reaches the third compartment (C) in a much softer form, and is then passed to the fourth, or rennet stomach, where it is still further softened and liquefied by the action of gastric juices.

Different stomachs for different jobs. ABOVE: Fishes which swallow their prey whole. CENTER: Stomachs which do the work of teeth. BELOW: The four compartments which break up the cellulose in the cow's diet of grass and herbs.

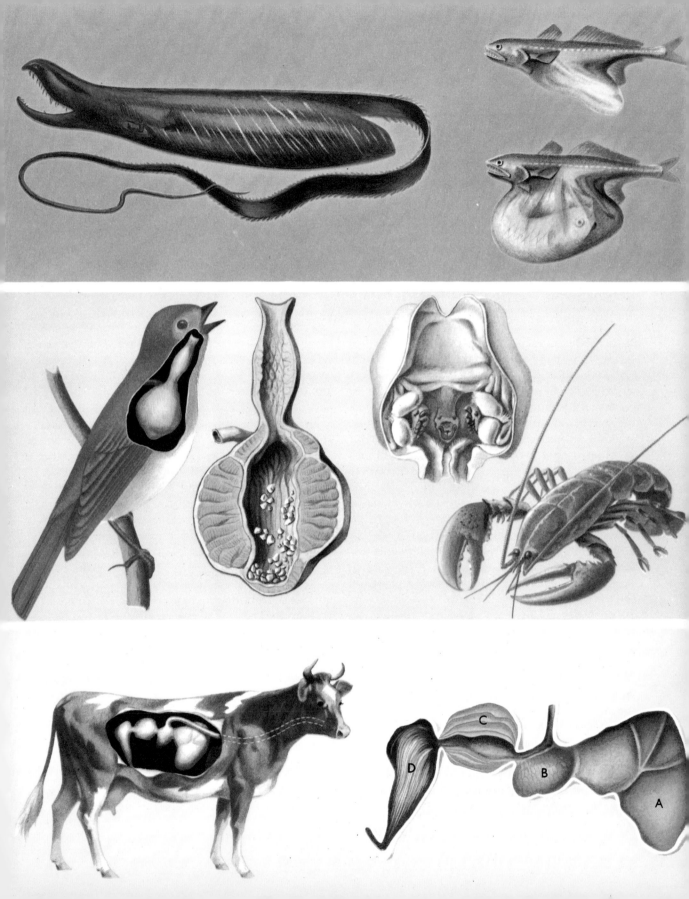

The Journey Through the Alimentary Canal

With the help of the top left-hand diagram we can follow the long journey which food makes through the alimentary canal, or food canal, of our own bodies. The diagram on the right is a reminder of the work which goes on in various parts of the canal, and it also shows how much, proportionately, each part contributes towards producing 14 pints of digestive juices daily.

First the food is cut up and ground by the action of the teeth. Then, pressed against the palate by the tongue, it is moistened and softened by juices from the salivary glands (1 and 2). There are three different kinds — those under the tongue, those near the hinge of the jaw, and those near the inner ear — and each produces a different kind of salivary juice.

Now, in a softened state, the food slides down the ten-inch long gullet (3) into the stomach (4). During its stay there, gastric juices produced at the rate of over six pints a day soften it still further, turning it into a kind of paste. From time to time a valve opens and allows small quantities of this paste to pass to the curving tube of the duodenum (9). Two small pipes lead into the duodenum, one from the liver (7) and another from the pancreas (8).

The liver, just below and towards the right of the ribs, is the largest gland-organ in the whole body, weighing between three and four pounds, and carries a complicated network of tiny bile canals and blood vessels. Each day it produces about a pint and three-quarters of bile, most of which collects in the gall-bladder (6) before passing through the bile-duct (5) into the duodenum. One of the parts the liver plays in digestion is to help turn vegetable starch into animal starch, or glycogen. The pancreas, roughly oblong in shape, produces an alkaline fluid which helps to convert starch into sugar and solid fats into glycerine or fatty acids. It also produces insulin which controls the way the body makes use of sugar.

Soaked with bile and pancreatic juice, the food-paste now passes on to the small intestine (10), which itself produces close to a pint of digestive juices each day. The small intestine contains many small cone-like structures which act as pumps, extracting most of the usable part of the food paste. It also has many muscles which expand and contract, pushing along the unusable food much as the squeezing of a tube pushes along toothpaste. Near the point where the food passes into the large intestine (13, 14 and 15) is an organ called the caecum (11) which ends in a kind of cul-de-sac called the appendix (12). The rising and descending parts (13 and 15) of the large intestine are attached to the fleshy wall of the abdomen. The crosswise part (14) is suspended by means of a fold from a large membrane called the peritoneum which envelops the whole of the intestines and the liver. The large intestine squeezes the unusable food along, extracting water from it on the way, towards the rectum (16) and the anus (17) where it is expelled from the body.

Water is important to the body since between 65 and 70 per cent of an adult's weight is made up of water.

The average adult needs about five pints of it every day, and he gets it from his solid foods (many of which contain a high proportion of water) as well as from what he drinks. Normally his body also expels about five pints of water a day. The diagram at the bottom left shows the daily balance sheet of water-income and water-expenditure. Income: 5 pints via the mouth; expenditure: 12½% via the lungs, 23% via the skin, 5½% via the intestines, and 59% via the kidneys.

TOP LEFT: The alimentary canal. RIGHT: The work that goes on in it and the percentage of digestive juices, out of 14 pints, different parts produce daily. BOTTOM LEFT: Water-income and water-expenditure in a single day.

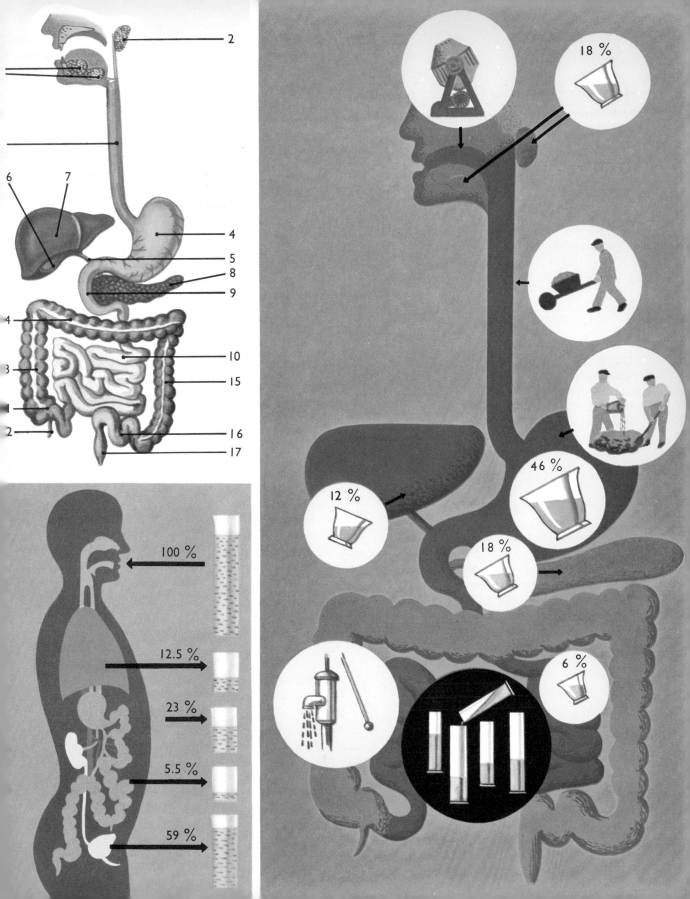

How Food passes into the Bloodstream

We have seen how food travels through the alimentary canal, but we have not yet considered how the body makes use of it. In fact our bodies cannot make use of food to produce warmth and energy or to help with the work of building and repairing body tissues until it has passed into the bloodstream.

While food is in the stomach it is already turning into a pulp, but it is not yet soft and pulpy enough to pass through the wall of the stomach into the blood. Besides, almost the whole of the inner surface of the stomach is covered with glands which pour digestive juices into the stomach. This current of juices is flowing the wrong way to encourage food particles to travel outwards through the stomach wall.

Two things must happen before any of the food-paste, or chyme, which leaves the stomach can pass into the blood. First it must be still further softened and liquefied, and next it must meet encouragement to flow from the inside of the alimentary canal towards the outside. The first of these things begins to happen as soon as bile from the liver and juices from the pancreas mix with the chyme. They act on it and turn part of it into a milky substance called chyle. It is this substance, still mixed with less usable food materials, which travels through the small intestine, and it is there that the chyle passes into the bloodstream.

We saw on the previous page how very long the small intestine is. Even if it were perfectly smooth it would have a very considerable inside surface area. But in fact much of the inside of the small intestine is covered with small, finger-like projections made up of many folds, and these increase the surface area enormously. These projections, called villi, vary in length from about one hundredth to one eighth of an inch. The top left-hand picture shows some in cross-section and the bottom picture shows some in lengthwise section. Both pictures are much enlarged.

These villi contain a network of fine vessels which absorb the chyle and also a network of tiny blood vessels. Within them the chyle can move in one direction only—from the chyle-absorbing vessels into the blood vessels. The circulation of the blood then carries essential body-building and energy foods, such as albumens and compounds of carbon, hydrogen and oxygen, to all parts of the body.

The large intestine has no villi, and unlike the small intestine, it produces no digestive juices. It can absorb food substances in small quantities, but normally it absorbs mainly water. Much of the material passing into the large intestine consists of food remains which the body cannot assimilate, including the woody, cellulose cell-walls of vegetable foods. A great number of bacteria, which live in a mutually useful partnership with man inside his intestine, help to break down these food remains and to keep them moving through the body. They also help to protect man from invasions by other bacteria which are harmful to him.

The bottom left-hand picture shows clearly that the wall of the intestine contains layers of two different kinds of muscles. Contraction of the lengthwise muscles extends the intestine. Contraction of the circular muscles shortens it. In man the intestine lengthens and shortens about seven times a minute; in a dog from eleven to twenty-two times; in a cat from twenty to thirty times.

When we consider how important and extensive the work of the intestines is, it is hardly surprising they are so long. The right-hand picture shows the lengths of the intestines of various animals compared with the lengths of their whole bodies. The dog's intestine is 4½ times as long as his body; man's 7 times; the pig's 15 times; the cow's 20 times; the sheep's 24 times. Generally speaking, flesh-eaters have the shortest intestines, vegetarian creatures the longest.

LEFT: The finger-like villi of the small intestine, in cross-section (above) and lengthwise (below).
RIGHT: Lengths of intestine of various animals compared with lengths of their bodies.

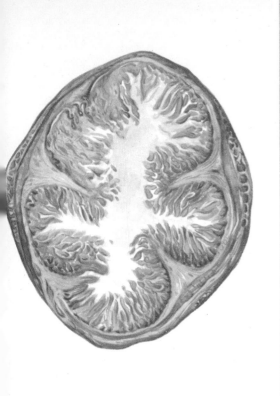

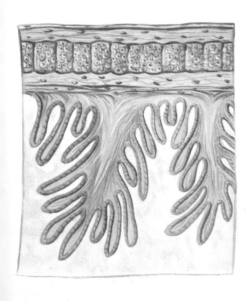

Energy from the Sun, Food from Plants, Power for Animals

The great processes which go to make up life are so complex, so intricately interwoven one with another, that we cannot always study them satisfactorily in isolation, as we can the chemical and physical processes of the inanimate world. Even while a plant or animal is in process of active growth — and in many plants this extends over a whole lifetime — parts of it are also decaying or wearing out. And for every living thing life involves constant change. So it sometimes happens that we can best understand certain aspects of life if we look at them, as it were, from a distance without attempting to pick out every detail, just as we would look at a broad landscape.

Perhaps that is the best way to take a first look at how plant and animal life are woven together. Plants and animals both need the same substances to provide them with energy and to enable them to grow and replace worn-out tissues. What we may term the fuel substances, needed for energy and warmth, consist mainly of fats and carbohydrates, such as starches and sugars. Proteins, which are more complex substances, provide the raw material for growth and replacement.

But whereas green plants can make these substances for themselves, animals cannot. They are all directly or indirectly dependent on green plants for every mouthful of food they eat. When we see a cow grazing in a meadow or a caterpillar eating a green leaf it is quite obvious that they owe their lives to plants. If, on the other hand, we chance to see a fox eating a hare, it is not so obvious. Yet the flesh-eating fox is just as dependent on plants as the vegetarian cow or caterpillar, for without vegetable food the hare itself would not have lived to provide the fox with its meal.

Through its leaves the green plant takes in carbon dioxide from the air. Through its roots it absorbs water from the soil. These two simple compounds between them contain the three chemical elements — carbon, hydrogen and oxygen — of which all carbohydrates are made. The plant also takes in through its roots small quantities of nitrogen salts and other minerals, and these provide it with the other ingredients of protein foods. But the plant can recombine the non-living ingredients it absorbs into living food materials only because it is equipped with a vast number of miniature factories — its green chlorophyll cells. These derive their power directly from the sun's rays.

This process is called photosynthesis, which means putting together by means of light. The sun provides the energy, the plant uses it to manufacture food, and either the plant or the animal which eats it once more converts the food into energy. When we burn coal we are releasing energy which the tree-ferns of the great coal forests stored up more than 250,000,000 years ago.

Our top pictures show three different plants and where they store reserve food supplies: the apple tree in its fruit, the flower in its bulb, the wheat in its grain. In each right-hand picture black represents the container, yellow the food supply, red the seed which, as it were, carries the train of life forward. The bottom picture reminds us how we ourselves use one of these food-stores, the wheat grain.

Plants can live without animals but not animals without plants. Indeed, plants grew on the earth millions of years before the first animals lived. Nevertheless, animal life does help plant life in many ways. As we saw earlier, animals breathe out carbon dioxide which green leaves need to take from the air; and animal manure or dead animal bodies in the soil provide substances which bacteria break down into nitrogen salts. When these salts dissolve, plants can absorb them through their roots.

ABOVE: Where three plants store the food which they make with the help of the sun's energy. BELOW: How man makes use of one of nature's great food stores, the wheat germ.

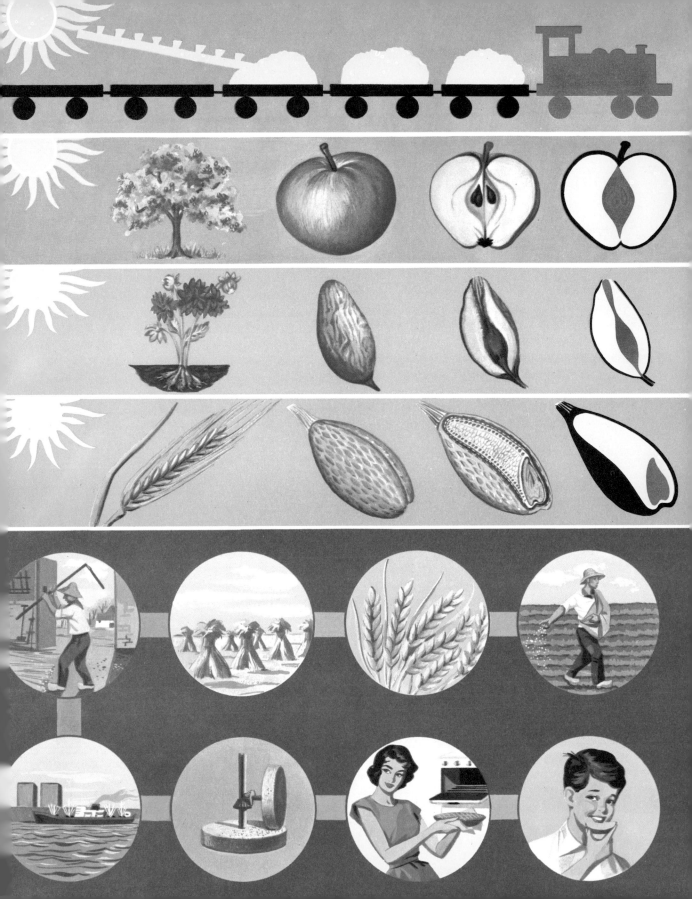

Creatures which Live without Oxygen

Quite early in our schooldays we learn that men, like all other mammals, cannot live long unless they have oxygen to breathe. Indeed, even green plants which give out oxygen as a by-product of photosynthesis, must also take in oxygen in the process of breathing. Yet there are several exceptions to the general rule that oxygen is necessary to life. Certain small animals called solitary worms, as well as other intestinal parasites, pass their lives in surroundings where oxygen is not normally present, yet they still flourish.

It remains true, however, that animals which can live without oxygen are extremely rare. Most of the living things which can do so are on that lowest level of life where it is very difficult to distinguish plants from animals. Almost all the higher plants and animals convert food into energy by means of chemical changes which need oxygen, but these small organisms derive energy from chemical changes which go on without oxygen. A typical example is a variety of bacteria found in milk. These transform the sugar content of milk into the lactic acid, which turns it sour.

It is interesting to see just how much the higher animals, and man himself, owes to such lowly forms of life. As industries grow up and populations increase, it sometimes happens that streams and rivers become polluted. The water is robbed of its natural supply of oxygen and soon most of the fishes die. But not every living thing dies. Indeed, there are specialists who can tell just how badly the water is polluted by noting which kinds of minute creatures still survive in it. However dirty the water may be, they will usually find certain bacteria. A few of them are shown, vastly enlarged, at the top of the opposite page. Some look like small straight sticks, some are equipped with whip-like tails, some even resemble small trees.

These bacteria can live without oxygen because they get their energy by breaking down dead organic matter into simpler compounds — sometimes into simple mineral salts. Together with water and carbon dioxide, these salts provide the materials from which single-cell plants called algae can manufacture food. Once algae begin to multiply in the water, single-cell animals can find food there. Then, in turn, small shellfish and the larvae of insects can live on the single-cell animals and the algae. These provide food for fishes, and so long as there is no further severe pollution, life in the stream can eventually return to normal.

A particularly active type of bacteria is that found in hay. It can raise the temperature of a moist hay-rick to about 60° Centigrade (140° Fahrenheit), and if the rick is very moist the temperature may become so high that it begins to smolder. Far more useful to man are yeast cells. It is not true to say that they can live without oxygen, but it is true that they can live where there is no free oxygen. They are able to take the oxygen they need from sugar, leaving behind alcohol and carbon dioxide. For many centuries man has used yeast (which grows naturally on many fruit skins) to make wine and beer. The quality of the yeast affects the flavor, the quality and the marketing price of wines and beers. Today many breweries have their own specially-bred varieties of yeast cells which they guard as their most prized trade secret.

Perhaps even before he made his first fermented liquor man used yeast in bread-making. When he kneaded the dough he added a little yeast to make the bread rise. Though he was not aware of it, the yeast cells took oxygen from the starchy dough, leaving alcohol and carbon dioxide. It was the bubbles of carbon dioxide in the dough that made the bread rise. The alcohol was driven out by the heat of the oven.

TOP: A polluted stream and bacteria which bring life back to it. BOTTOM: A hay-rick becomes hot, dough rises, beer ferments — all the work of lowly forms of life.

Plants which Trap and Eat Insects

There are a number of interesting exceptions to another general rule of life — the rule that green plants make their own food from non-living substances. Many plants grow in poor soil which contains insufficient nitrogen to provide them with all the food-producing materials they need. Some of them make good the deficiency by eating insects.

Because they *are* plants, rooted in the ground and compelled to live in one place, they cannot hunt for their prey as animals can. Instead they have developed various ingenious traps to catch their victims, and some of these bear a striking resemblance to the animal traps which man himself uses.

Most of the insect-eating plants live in hot countries but there are also some in the United States. One is the sundew, shown in the top picture, which is found in humid heathlands. The outer part of its flowers, growing very near the ground, are made up of many fine glandular hairs. From these hairs a gum-like liquid oozes out which sparkles in the sun like drops of dew, and gives the plant its name.

Any small insect which ventures onto these hairs is caught just as certainly as if it had landed on a man-made fly-paper. First the sticky liquid holds it fast, then the hairs close up. The liquid is not merely a kind of glue to hold the insect fast, it is also a digestive juice like the pepsin which breaks down protein foods inside our own bodies. Very soon the insect is transformed into substances which the sundew can absorb and use for its own nourishment.

The tropical pitcher plant, shown in the second picture, employs a very different kind of trap, which works in the same way as the pitfalls that early men dug to catch fierce wild animals. From the tip of its big green leaf grows a kind of cord which supports what is really a second part of the leaf — a strange structure like a small vase with an open lid. This vase, often brightly colored in reds, browns and greens, is covered with honey glands around its lip and under the lid. There are many species and the capacity of the pitcher varies from the size of a thimble to that of a quart jar. But the insect that goes here in search of honey is doomed. It can get no hold on the smooth, slippery surface of the vase, and falls to the bottom which is full of digestive fluids.

Some three hundred years ago many botanists were fond of moralizing about plants. They regarded plants, which make their food from raw materials in the soil and the air, as somehow superior to animals which can live only by taking the life of plants or of other animals. It must have come as a shock to them when, in 1679, John Ellis wrote to the great Swedish naturalist Linnaeus describing the habits of the plant shown in the bottom picture.

It is the Venus fly-trap, which Ellis had seen in Florida. The top part of each leaf is arranged in two halves, like a half-open book. Around the edge of each "page" are a number of sharp spikes. On the surface there are many tiny red points, which are the tips of digestive glands, and near the center of the "page" are three very fine sensitive hairs. When an insect visits the plant, it has only to touch one of these hairs and the two halves of the leaf snap together in an instant. The spikes around the edges interlock making escape impossible, and the insect is quickly covered with digestive juices from the glands on the inner surface of the leaf.

So the Venus fly-trap catches its prey by the same kind of method that man employs in rat traps and in the snares he sometimes sets for the fur-bearing wild animals of northern forests.

Plants which set traps as man does. The sundew (top) acts like a sticky fly-paper, the pitcher plant (center) like a pitfall, the Venus fly-trap (bottom) like a spiked snare.

Three Kinds of Breathing Apparatus

We all spend a great part of our waking life moving about — walking, running, cycling, playing games. Where do we get our motive power from? The answer is from the food we eat and the air we breathe. We saw earlier that all except a very few animals must breathe oxygen. This oxygen must pass into the blood. Then as the blood circulates, it carries the oxygen to all the cells of the animal's body. There it combines with food substances containing carbon and produces warmth, energy and carbon dioxide. The carbon dioxide is absorbed into the blood, and from the blood it must pass into the outside air.

All the higher animals have specialized breathing organs whose job is to allow oxygen to pass from the air into the blood, and carbon dioxide to pass from the blood into the air. The bigger the surface-area of the breathing organ the more efficiently it does its job. The top left-hand picture shows a fish with its gill-cover removed so as to display the gills — the fish's breathing organ. The diagram below shows that the gills, made of thin blades like the underside of a mushroom, have a huge surface area. These blades all contain blood-vessels. As water flows over them, oxygen from the water passes through the thin walls of the gill-blades into the blood-vessels, here shown clear red; blood-vessels shown bluish red bring the blood containing carbon dioxide back to the gills. When a fish is taken out of water its gills stick together. Their surface area is then not large enough to allow much oxygen to enter the bloodstream, so the fish suffocates although there is air all around it.

The worm shown in the picture lives in the sand by the sea. It, too, has gill-like structures, which it carries on its back.

If you looked at an insect under a microscope, you would see that it has little holes on the outside of its body. These holes are the entrances to tiny breathing tubes which branch out inside the body, as shown in the picture. When a bee or a wasp expands its body, air containing oxygen is drawn into the tubes; when it contracts its body, air containing carbon dioxide is pushed out.

This system works well with insects because the outside of the body is hard and horny. But a soft-skinned land animal would find such a system useless, since the tubes would easily dry up. Such animals commonly have lungs which are inside the chest where they cannot easily become dry. When the ribs move up and out (see bottom diagram) the lungs expand, and fresh air is drawn into them. When the ribs move inwards the lungs are compressed, pushing out the used air. To increase their surface area, the lungs have many folds (see top pictures). Lizards have more of these folds than salamanders and frogs, and mammals have many more still.

Humans and other mammals breathe air into the lungs through the windpipe which leads from the nose and throat. This pipe divides into two bronchial tubes, which themselves divide, branching and branching again to all parts of the lungs. The very smallest branches end in tiny air-sacs whose walls are surrounded by many fine blood-vessels. Here oxygen is transferred from the air to the blood and carbon dioxide from the blood to the air.

The lungs expand and contract with a regular rhythm. When resting, we breathe about fifteen times a minute and take in just under a pint of air at each breath — about 12 pints per minute. When we are doing strenuous exercise we need more oxygen to help produce more energy. When walking we take in about 24 pints of air a minute, when cycling fast about 72 pints, when swimming about 96 pints, and when rock-climbing about 120 pints.

TOP LEFT: Gills of a fish and a sea-worm. BOTTOM: An insect's air tubes. TOP RIGHT: Lung-folds of four different animals. BOTTOM RIGHT: Human lungs, and how air-intake varies with different activities.

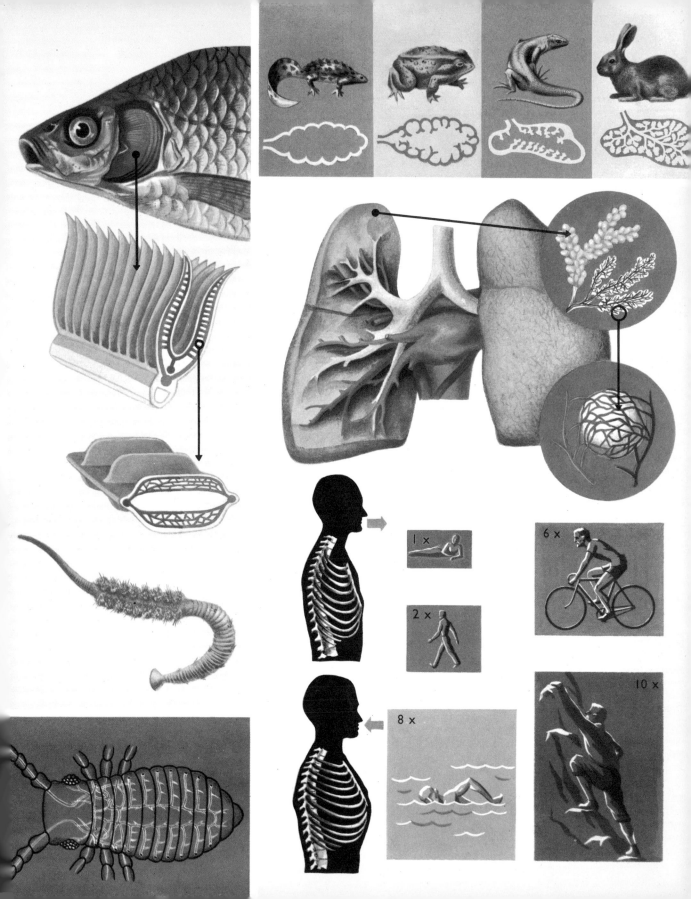

How Plants Exchange Gases With the Outside Air

In breathing it is the oxygen from the air that plays the most important part. The much larger volume of nitrogen merely dilutes the oxygen, just as we sometimes use water to dilute acids. When animals or plants breathe, they take in oxygen, combine it with carbon in their cells, and give out carbon dioxide.

In plants this breathing process goes on night and day, and all parts of the plant — roots and stem as well as leaves — constantly take in small quantities of oxygen and give out small quantities of carbon dioxide. But in daylight directly the opposite exchange of gases goes on as well. In order to manufacture its food, the plant must take in large quantities of carbon dioxide to combine with water from the soil, and in the food-making process it produces large quantities of oxygen which it gives off to the outside air.

So the picture at the top right shows two ways in which man (and, indeed, all the animal world) is indebted to plants. Not only do they store up the food which man lives on, but they also keep the air fit for him to breathe by taking suffocating carbon dioxide from it and replenishing its vital supply of oxygen.

On the underside of a leaf there are vast numbers of specialized cells which help the plant to exchange gases with the outside air. They play no special part in breathing (and indeed they close up at night), but they are vitally important to the other exchange of gases which a plant makes during daylight hours. The top left-hand picture shows a few of these pea-shaped cells, which cluster round the network of veins, greatly enlarged. You can form some idea of their real size from the fact that a leaf as big as the palm of your hand may contain five million of them.

It is possible to do several simple but interesting experiments to show just how a plant exchanges gases with the outside air. We know that the air we breathe out of our lungs is moist. So is the air a plant gives out. If we completely cover a growing plant with a dry glass bell-jar, small beads of water gradually form on the inside of the glass. The plant combines some of the oxygen it takes in with hydrogen to form water. Its leaves also give out some of the water taken in through the roots.

Now look at the picture at the bottom left. If, during daylight, we leave a water plant in a glass of water and place a funnel upside down dipping into the water, we find that oxygen bubbles up through the funnel. (We can show that it *is* oxygen because it will make a glowing wood splint burst into flame.) The water plant has taken in carbon dioxide and given off oxygen, in its food-producing process of photosynthesis.

The top right-hand pictures on the blue background show a very different experiment. Here we completely enclose a plant in a sealed jar for five days *and leave it in the dark so that no photosynthesis goes on.* Then, when we plunge a lighted candle into the jar, the flame goes out. The plant has breathed in all the oxygen and given off carbon dioxide. (If we simply leave an empty jar in the dark for five days it will not extinguish a candle flame.)

The final experiment (bottom right) is also concerned with a plant kept in darkness. We bubble air through lime-water in the first jar, to remove all carbon dioxide. This air enters the second jar, where the plant is kept in darkness. Air from the second jar is then passed into the third jar, which contains clear lime-water. The lime-water turns chalky, because the plant has produced carbon dioxide which combines with the lime to produce chalk.

TOP LEFT: Cells which enable a plant to exchange gases. TOP RIGHT: Plants at once supply food and purify the air. BOTTOM: Experiments to test what gases plants give out.

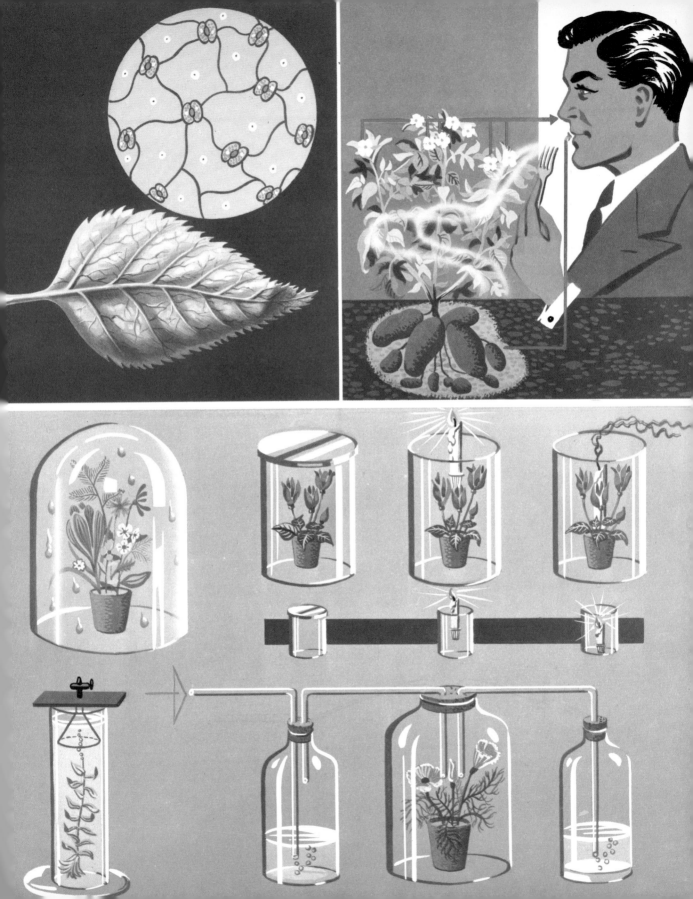

Blood—its vital part in all Animal Life

Animals constantly breathe in oxygen and breathe out carbon dioxide and water vapor. The ceaseless exchange of gases is carried out in the bloodstream by an ingredient in many of the blood cells called hemoglobin. This substance, which gives the blood its color, easily absorbs oxygen but easily parts with it again to carbon and hydrogen.

Look at the left-hand column of pictures. In each the test-tube stands for the top figure of a fraction and the weight for the bottom figure. The whole fraction shows how much of the creature's weight is made up of blood. In human beings, sheep and elephants, blood accounts for a fifteenth of the total weight; in pigeons for a twelfth; in frogs for a seventeenth. In the small snake-like salamander shown in the bottom picture it accounts for one twenty-first part.

In the course of a single day the heart of an adult human being beats a hundred thousand times. All the blood in the body is pumped through it over and over again — a total of more than 17,000 pints. In one day's pumping the heart does as much work as a man would do in carrying a 150 lb. bag of coal to the top of the Eiffel Tower, nearly 1,000 feet high.

If you were to smear a little blood on a glass slide and examine it through a microscope the first thing you would notice would probably be a great number of tiny disc-shaped cells, flattened in the middle. These discs, which contain the vital hemoglobin, are called the red blood cells. But if you had a very powerful microscope and could examine them separately, you would find that they are actually light yellow. It is only their great concentration in the blood which makes them appear darker.

The red blood cells (numbered 1 in the top right picture) are so small that 125 of them placed side by side would stretch only one millimeter. The figures under the weights in the left-hand pictures show how many red blood cells a single cubic millimeter of the blood of each creature contains. For sheep the figure is over 13,000,000. For men it is about 5,000,000. For women about 4,500,000.

A man of average weight has over nine pints of blood, containing 25 *trillion* red blood cells. Tiny as they are, if they were threaded together like a string of beads they would stretch one-and-a-quarter times around the earth (center right).

The size and shape of the red blood cells are different in different creatures. The yellow discs in the left-hand pictures show how they vary. They are largest in the salamander and smallest in the sheep. In men, elephants and pigeons they are not very different in size. In all these creatures the red blood cells have one strange thing in common. While they are being formed in the bone marrow they have a nucleus, like most other cells; but when they enter the bloodstream this nucleus has disappeared.

The white blood cells (2 in the top right-hand picture) are similar to the ameba we saw on page 17, and they engulf harmful bacteria in our bodies just as the ameba engulfs its food. They are larger than the red blood cells and a cubic millimeter of our blood normally contains only 6,000 to 8,000 of them. When we have an infectious disease their numbers may increase considerably.

The minute bodies numbered 3 in the top right-hand picture are the blood-platelets, probably composed of cell fragments. They contain a substance called fibrinogen. When we cut ourselves, this enables the blood to clot and prevent excessive bleeding.

Not all animals have red blood. The bottom right-hand picture shows, by colored backgrounds, some with red, some with yellow-orange, some with bluish, some with greenish and some with almost colorless blood.

LEFT: Blood statistics of six different creatures. RIGHT: (Top) Main constituents of human blood. (Center) How blood cells of one man would stretch round the earth. (Bottom) Animals and their blood-coloring.

= 13.190.000

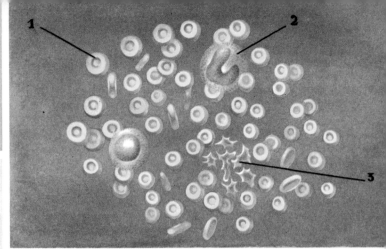

= 5.000.000   = 4.500.000

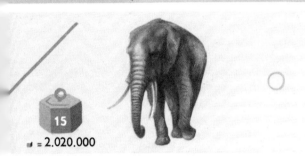

= 2.4000.000

= 2.020.000

= 400.000

= 36.000

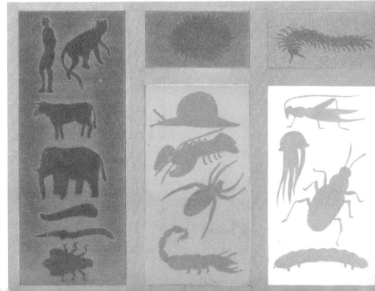

Ensuring that Blood is Life-Giving

If we meet with some accident and lose a great deal of blood, the exchange of gases which the body needs may not go on at the right rate to keep us healthy. If the loss of blood is very severe we may even die. Today the lives of many victims of accidents are saved by injections of blood given by healthy blood-donors.

Many years ago there were doubtless just as many people willing to give blood to save the lives of others as there are today. But until comparatively recent times the gift of blood did not always succeed in saving a life. Sometimes it hastened the death of the sick person. As long ago as the eighteenth century some lives were saved by blood-transfusions, but others were certainly lost, too.

Among the men who discovered the explanation of the mystery was an Austrian named Dr. Landsteiner (top left). He found that there are at least four different blood-groups to which different human beings belong, and that the mixing of blood from people of different groups can sometimes cause fatal results. Today the four main groups are known everywhere as A, B, AB and O, and although it is rather complicated, it is worth trying to understand how they differ.

In all except one group (group O) the blood cells contain substances named agglutinogens A or B. In all except one other group (group AB) the *plasma* — the fluid part of the blood, excluding the blood cells — contains substances named agglutinins anti-A or anti-B. Group A contains agglutinogen A and agglutinin anti-B. If blood containing agglutinogen B is mixed with blood containing agglutinin anti-B, its cells stick together, and the result may well prove fatal. Blood of group B is exactly opposite to blood of group A. It contains agglutinogen B and agglutinin anti-A.

The bottom diagram shows what blood-transfusions are safe between members of different groups. You will see that blood of group A (red) may be given to groups A and AB but never to B. Blood of group B (green) may be given to groups B and AB, but never to A.

Blood of group AB contains both kinds of agglutinogens. It cannot safely be given to group A, B or O, but only to members of its own group. On the other hand, blood of group O, which contains no agglutinogens, can safely be given to people belonging to any blood group, but it may not receive blood from any group except its own.

If you think hard about the last statement you may notice something very strange about it. Blood of group O contains both agglutinins but no agglutinogens. If other kinds of blood, which *do* contain agglutinogens, are mixed with it — even in small quantities — the result is harmful. But if it is passed itself, in small quantities, into bloodstreams which contain agglutinogens, its agglutinin content does no harm.

This is extremely important. It means that blood plasma which contains *only* agglutinins, can safely be given in small amounts to any blood group.

In 1914 the Belgian Professor Hustin (top right) discovered that the coagulation of blood could be prevented by adding to it sodium citrate. This made possible indirect transfusion and for the donor's blood to be kept for 2-3 weeks. Today, blood plasma (prepared by "spinning" blood, somewhat as wet clothes are treated in a spin-dryer) can be preserved and stored for use when needed. It is not so effective as whole blood, but greatly helps in overcoming shock from loss of blood.

Research still goes on and scientists have recently discovered various types of human blood (M, N, MN and Rh). Medical research workers now seek substances which can be kept far longer than plasma without deteriorating.

TOP: Blood transfusion. Dr. Landsteiner (left) and Professor Hustin (right) helped change it from a gamble to a safe operation. BOTTOM: Color key shows transfusions between different blood-groups which can be safely undertaken.

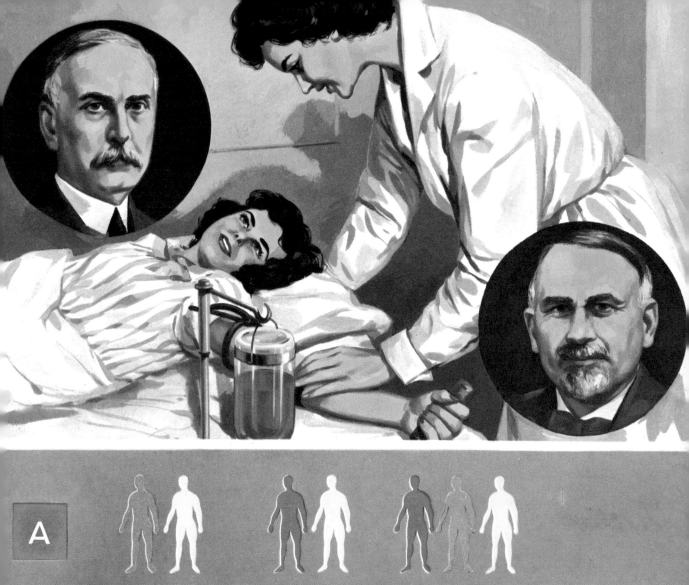

A

B

AB

0

The Pumping and Purifying of the Blood

In all backboned animals the blood constantly circulates through a closed circuit made up of veins, heart and arteries. The top left-hand diagram shows the process in very simple form.

The heart is shown as a pump. The blood (shown dark red) which flows into it through veins from all parts of the body, is charged with carbon dioxide. This blood, pumped through arteries by the heart, reaches a purifying station (the lungs or gills) where carbon dioxide is removed and where the blood is recharged with oxygen. The purified blood (now shown orange) flows on its way to all parts of the body. There its oxygen combines with food substances to produce carbon dioxide. This blood, again carrying carbon dioxide, returns through veins to the heart, ready for the next circular trip.

The diagram below shows, again very simply, the network of vessels that carry the blood on its journey. Big arteries with strong walls lead away from the heart, branching out into more and more smaller arteries with thinner and thinner walls, where the blood flows more slowly. The return flow, from cells all over the body, begins in a network of thin-walled veins. These meet like tributaries of a great river system, and the blood continues to flow through fewer and fewer big veins, with thicker walls, back to the heart.

The vital pump of the heart and the layout of the circulatory system are different in different kinds of backboned animals. Let us look first at the fish, the earliest backboned animal ever to live on our earth. The diagram shows that its heart has a single inlet chamber, the auricle (1) which receives impure blood from the veins, and a single outlet chamber, the ventricle (2) from which blood flows on through large arteries (3 and 4). After traveling through many tiny blood vessels it reaches the gills where it is oxygenated, and then passes through more large arteries (5

and 6). Branches of these arteries lead towards the head (7), the kidneys (10), the intestines (11), the liver (12), the pectoral fin (13) and the ventral fin (14). Veins (8 and 9) carry the impure blood from these parts back to the heart.

The frog is a representative of the amphibians, the first backboned animals to live on land as well as in water. The top diagram shows the layout of its heart. (Like the other diagrams below, it is shown as if its owner were facing us, so when we refer to the left part of the heart we are referring to the right side of the diagram, and *vice versa*.) The frog's heart has two auricles (the smaller lobes, at the top) but only one ventricle. The right-hand auricle passes impure blood into the ventricle, and the left-hand one passes oxygenated blood. So the ventricle contains a mixture, which it pumps through a branching artery, part to the lungs and part to the rest of the body.

The hearts of reptiles, the first backboned animals to be independent of the water, are more complex. There are two auricles and a ventricle which is almost, but not completely, divided into two. Oxygenated blood from the lungs enters through the left auricle; impure blood from the veins enters through the right auricle. Because the ventricle is not completely divided, both kinds of blood can mingle in it. The artery which leads from the right of the heart up towards the lungs carries impure blood which has mingled only a little with oxygenated blood. The artery which leads from the left-hand side down towards other parts of the body carries mainly oxygenated blood which has mingled only a little with impure blood.

The bottom diagram shows the heart of a bird. It has two separate auricles and two quite separate ventricles. By following the arrows you can see how oxygenated blood *only* enters from the lungs and passes to other parts of the body, and how impure blood *only* enters from the other parts of the body and is pumped to the lungs.

TOP LEFT: Simplified scheme of typical blood circulation system. BOTTOM LEFT: How a fish's blood circulates. RIGHT: Hearts and circulation systems of a frog, a reptile and a bird.

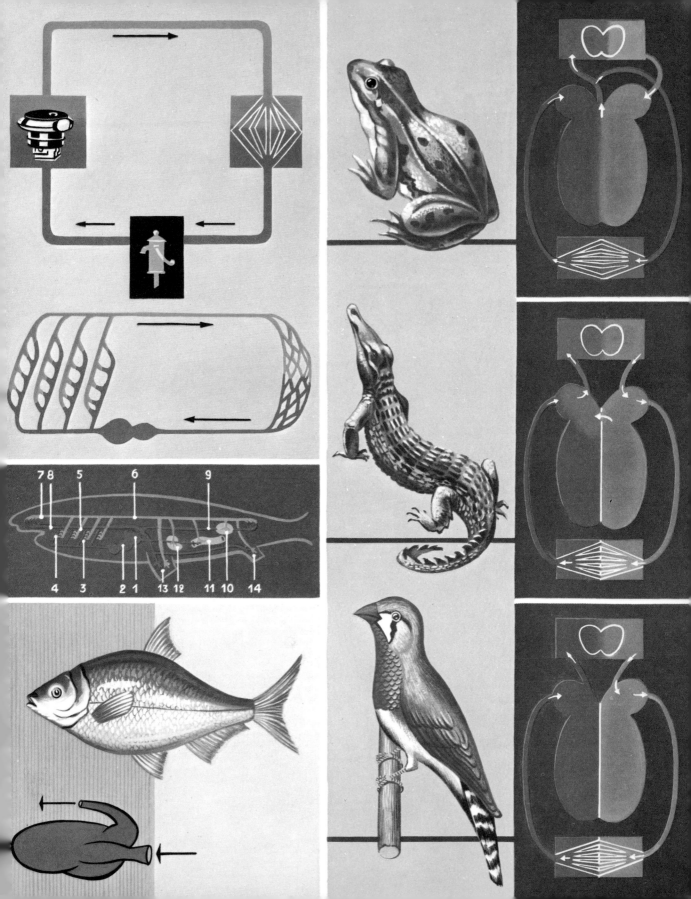

7 8 5 6 9
4 3 2 1 13 12 11 10 14

Discovering the Circulation of Blood in Man

When we remember that the first civilizations, in Mesopotamia and Egypt, date back more than five thousand years, it is strange to think that man did not understand how his own blood circulates until little more than three centuries ago.

The ancient Egyptians learned a great deal about human anatomy in the houses of the dead, where bodies were embalmed. Much of their knowledge in time reached the Greeks and the Romans. The latter, who encouraged surgeons to operate on soldiers injured on the field of battle, doubtless added to it. But in medieval Europe the Church frowned on the cutting up of dead bodies and even, to some extent, on surgery. Medical men still relied largely on works which Aristotle wrote in the fourth century B.C., and Galen in the second century A.D.

Among the first to break away from these restrictions was Andreas Vesalius, a Belgian, who was professor of anatomy at the great medical school of Padua. He added to and corrected his knowledge of anatomy by cutting up and carefully examining dead bodies, and in 1543 he published an entirely new kind of textbook on anatomy, illustrated by one of the finest artists of his day. Like many men before him, he knew that the blood moves in the body because of the action of the heart, but he did not understand how. The drawings of bones, muscles and sinews in his book were remarkably accurate, but the diagrams of how the blood moves in veins and arteries were very wide of the mark.

His book, however, stimulated others to go on with the work he had started. One of them, Fabricius, discovered that veins contain valves which allow the blood to flow only one way—towards the heart. Just before 1600 a young Englishman, William Harvey (top left), went to Padua to study under Fabricius. In the new tradi-tion of Padua, Harvey not only examined dead bodies but also conducted experiments with live animals, and he finally established how the blood circulates.

Fabricius already knew that blood in the veins travels only towards the heart. Harvey discovered that blood in the arteries travels only away from the heart. He learned, too, that the heart does not draw in blood from the veins when it expands, as expanding lungs draw in air. On the contrary, when the muscles of the heart move in such a way as to lessen the space inside it, the heart acts like a pump and forces blood into the arteries. When the muscles perform the opposite kind of movement the capacity of the heart increases. Blood cannot flow backward along the arteries to fill the extra space, but it can and does flow forward from the veins into the heart.

It is easy to see why Harvey's experiments on live animals were important. Before those experiments many people thought that arteries did not contain blood at all. Indeed, they are normally empty after death, because they have passed blood on to the veins and have received none from the heart to replace it.

Look at the cross-section through the human heart opposite. Oxygenated blood is pumped from the top of the left ventricle (lower orange), through the great artery called the aorta, then through a series of smaller arteries and capillaries to all parts of the body. Another series of capillary veins and larger veins carry the now impure blood back to the right atrium (upper red).

This impure blood is pumped from the right ventricle (lower red), through the pulmonary artery, to the lungs. There it is reoxygenated, and returns through a series of ever-larger veins to the left atrium (upper orange), ready to be pumped once more to all parts of the body. The diagram on the right is no more than a rough sketch map, for in fact our bodies contain many thousands of tiny veins and arteries which it cannot possibly show.

LEFT: Vesalius, the first anatomist of modern times, and (above) William Harvey, discoverer of the circulation of the blood. RIGHT: Cross-section through human heart and map of circulatory system.

Aorta

Pulmonary Artery

R.A.

L.A.

R.V.

L.V.

ANDREAS VESALIUS

Sense of Taste and Sense of Smell

If we could not see, hear, taste, smell or feel anything, it is difficult to imagine how we could begin to be aware of the world around us. It is only by means of its senses that any animal makes contact with its environment. Not all animals have the same senses, or even the same number of senses, and a creature which is deficient in one frequently has another one which is extremely well developed.

Among the higher animals all the specialized sense organs—organs adapted to respond to stimuli produced by light, sound or chemicals—are situated in the head. The senses concerned especially with chemical stimuli are taste and smell. Perhaps this becomes most obvious when we think how the nose and mouth pass a quick, condemning judgment on many foods which are tainted or poisoned. But far more frequently they enable us to appreciate the complicated chemistry of good food or the volatile chemicals which account for the scent of flowers.

The tongue and the palate make up the seat of taste. The tongue is covered with tiny protrusions called taste buds (A), each composed of microscopic cells. It is only when food (C) is dissolved by saliva and reaches these taste buds that we begin to savor it.

The sense of taste by itself is not as discriminating as we might imagine. It distinguishes only four main groups of flavors—sweet, salt, bitter and sour—and different parts of the tongue specialize in perceiving different flavors. The front of the tongue, for instance, helps us to appreciate sweet flavors and the back bitter flavors.

Much of our enjoyment of food comes from our appreciation of the feel of various food-textures in our mouths. Even more, perhaps, comes from our sense of smell, which is far more sensitive than the unaided sense of taste, and which operates even at a distance.

In the nose there are three small openings, each covered by a mucous membrane furrowed by many tiny blood vessels. The lower two help to trap dust and disease germs and also to warm and moisten the air we breathe. The upper one is equipped with olfactory, or smell, cells covered with fine hairs. These cells are the final tiny branches of the olfactory nerve which, after passing through a sieve-like bone, leads to the brain.

How well developed an animal's sense of smell is depends largely on the extent of the olfactory membrane in the nose (shown at the tips of the arrows from B and C). In man, whose sense of smell is comparatively poor, this membrane is small. In the deer, as our pictures show, its surface is much larger because of many folds. In a dog, the surface area of the olfactory membrane is equal to about an eighteenth of the whole skin area of the body. In man it is only about one eight-thousandth part.

The center of the sense of smell is not invariably in the nose. Lizards and snakes can detect smells with their quick-darting tongues, and butterflies by means of their antennae. The sense of taste, too, is sometimes located where we might least expect. Certain insects, for instance, have their organs of taste at the tips of their legs. Butterflies have only to alight on an appetizing morsel to detect its flavor. There are even certain moths whose legs can detect the flavor of weak sugar-water which a man could not taste until it were made a hundred times stronger.

The fish opposite is a member of the sheat-fish family. It can sense prey passing near it by means of its tail. Its beard-like feelers (the tips are shown enlarged at Y) are equipped with taste buds. As the prey nears them, the fish turns around rapidly, seizes it and swallows it. These "taste-feelers" also enable the sheat-fish to hunt efficiently for food among small crevices in rocks.

TOP: The organs of taste and smell in man, and the more efficient organ of smell in the deer. BOTTOM: A fish which detects food with its tail and tastes it, with feelers, before eating it.

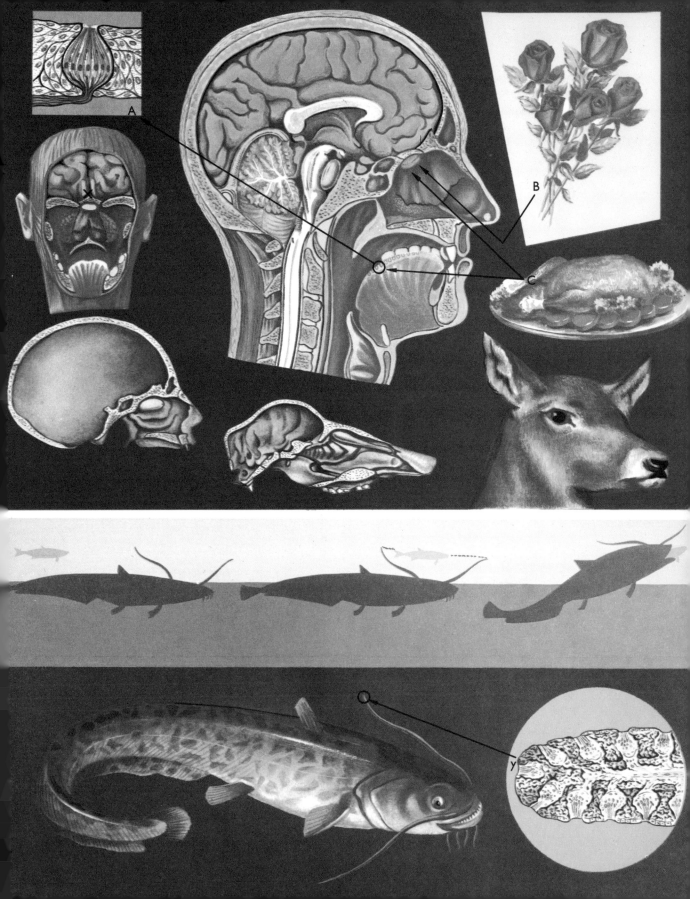

Knowing Light
From Darkness
and Really Seeing

Just as there are organs of taste and smell which cannot be called mouths or noses, so there are sense organs responding to light stimuli which cannot be called eyes.

If we place an earthworm in a glass tube partly covered with a roll of black paper, the worm will wriggle into the darkened part of the tube. If we then slide the paper along so that light falls on to the front of the worm only, the front very quickly withdraws into the shade. The back part of the worm responds to light in the same way, but more slowly. The center part is far less sensitive to light.

We cannot say that an earthworm sees things, but only that it can distinguish light from darkness. We certainly cannot say it has eyes, but only that it has organs sensitive to light.

Certain flatworms have more efficient light-organs called ocelli, which is Latin for little eyes. In those shown in the picture these "little eyes" are concentrated near the front of the head. Seen under a microscope, each looks like a little cup filled with black pigment and linked to a yellow visual cell beneath. Since the ocelli face different ways, the flatworm can not only tell light from darkness; it can also tell where the light is coming from, and this may help to give it some sense of direction.

It was probably from some such simple organs as these that two distinct classes of true eyes gradually evolved: the eyes of backboned animals and the equally wonderful but very different compound eyes of shellfish and insects.

The human eye, like that of most backboned animals, may be compared with a photographic camera, as shown in the diagram opposite. Near the front it has a lens (1) which forms reversed images on the sensitive plate or screen called the retina (3) at the back. Just as the camera is dark inside, so is the eye; but whereas the hollow part

of the camera contains only air, the part of the eyeball behind the lens is filled with a hard jelly-like substance which keeps the eye in shape.

The round eye, set in its oval socket, is moved by means of muscles, attached to its outer covering, or cornea. The greater part of the cornea (shown grey), including the part to which the muscles are joined, is opaque. Only the front part (shown white) is transparent. Not far behind this transparent part is a kind of extending curtain (shown brown) called the iris. It is the reflected light from the pigment particles of the iris which gives eyes their color—black, brown, grey, green or blue.

Muscles enable the iris to expand or contract rather like the regulating shutter of a good camera. In sunlight the iris covers most of the hole, or pupil (2), in front of the lens. In dim candlelight, it opens and the pupil becomes much larger. A cat has a reflector behind its retina. In dim light we can see some of the light which has entered its pupil reflected back again.

The small pictures above those of the sun and candle show that the lens of the eye, too, can change shape. When we look at a distant view, it is long and thin; when we read small print close up, it becomes shorter and thicker and so focuses differently. Our ability to distinguish between light of different wavelengths—that is, our ability to tell one color from another—depends on special cells of different kinds in the retina.

Insects' eyes (part of one is shown greatly enlarged) and also the eyes of many shellfish, are made up of separate divisions composed of light-sensitive cells. Some of these strange eyes give many separate pictures of an object, or parts of an object; others give a number of bright but overlapping pictures. Some insects seem able to distinguish clearly between different colors. The Vanessa butterfly, for instance, has a marked preference for red and almost always seeks out red flowers.

TOP: Two creatures which can merely tell light from darkness. CENTER: How the eye adjusts itself to near and distant vision, to bright light and dim. Its power to distinguish colors. BOTTOM: Reflecting eye of cat, an insect's eye, and an insect with color sense.

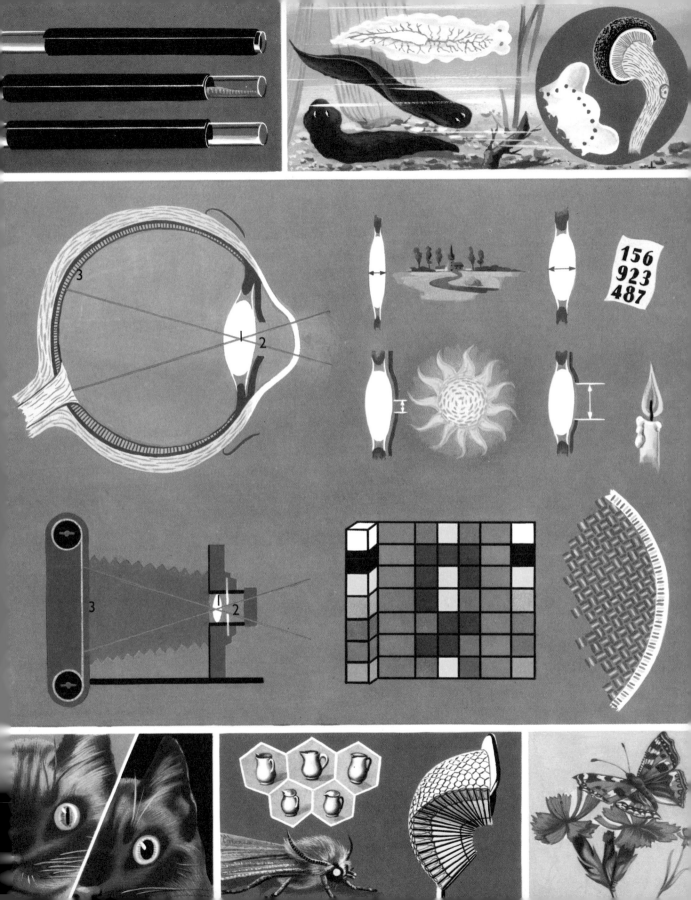

Registering Vibrations in the Air

When a drummer hits the tight-stretched skin of a drum, not only does that skin vibrate, but it also sets the air around it vibrating. Waves of alternating compressed air and rarefied air move outwards in all directions. The same happens when a sexton tolls a bell or when a guitarist twangs the string of a guitar. Indeed, almost any kind of movement made in air sets the air vibrating. Some vibrations move in long waves, only a few per second; others move in short waves, a great many per second. But, like tall soldiers taking long, slow steps and short soldiers taking short, quick steps, they all travel at the same speed.

Animals are made aware of many of these vibrations in the air by means of auditory, or sound-detecting organs. A cross-section through man's auditory organ, the ear, is shown opposite. Vibrations in the air reach first the trumpet-like outer ear (1) and are then directed through the auditory channel (2) to the ear-drum (3). The ear-drum begins to vibrate and sets three tiny bones (4) vibrating: the malleus (or hammer), the incus (or anvil) and the stapes (or stirrup). The small cavity behind the ear-drum is filled with air, and it connects with the area between the mouth and the gullet by means of the eustachian tube (5). This small tube is closed most of the time, but opens every time we swallow. The stirrup bone, as it vibrates, affects the snail-shaped cochlea (6) which holds the ends of the auditory nerve. This nerve carries the impulses to the brain, where they register as sounds.

The three semi-circular "canals", shown just above the cochlea, are filled with fluid which helps the passing-along of sound vibrations. They also contain the fine, hair-like ends of many nerve cells. The oval cavity to which the canals join contains small chalky grains called otoliths. These grains tend to stay still when the rest of the body moves. Thus if we turn quickly to the left they tap against nerve-ends to the right; if we turn quickly to the right, they tap against nerve-ends to the left. This greatly helps our sense of direction and balance.

The internal hearing organs of four classes of backboned animals — fish, amphibian, bird and mammal — are shown on the left. Only the rabbit, which is a mammal, has a snail-shaped inner ear rather like our own. The others show marked differences of shape.

The diagram on the right shows that not all animals can hear the same range of sounds. Bats, for instance, can hear extremely high-pitched sounds, caused by short-wave vibrations at the rate of 75,000 per second. Dogs and cats can hear vibrations at the rate of 40,000 per second. The average man cannot hear vibrations much faster than 20,000 per second. Lizards can hear only sounds of very low pitch.

Hearing organs take on many different forms. The ear-drum, for example, is not always well protected and well hidden. In the frog (bottom left) it is level with the skin. The cricket (extreme bottom) has ear-drums on its front legs. We saw earlier that many insects have a system of air-tubes which serve a similar purpose to our own lungs. The cricket's strangely-placed ear-drums are at the extremities of enlarged air-filled tubes of that kind.

Not many years ago, naturalists doubted whether any insects could hear. They imagined that male and female crickets, for example, were attracted to each other only by scent. As an experiment, a male cricket was shut up in one room and a female in another. A microphone in the male's room connected to a loudspeaker in the female's. As soon as the male began to chirp, the female moved towards the loudspeaker. Since that time it has been proved that a number of different insects have auditory organs.

TOP: *Human ear (right) and inner parts of hearing organs of four other backboned creatures (left).* BOTTOM: *Ear-drums of frog and cricket (left). Diagram showing which creatures hear highest sounds (right). The higher the number the higher the notes the creature can hear.*

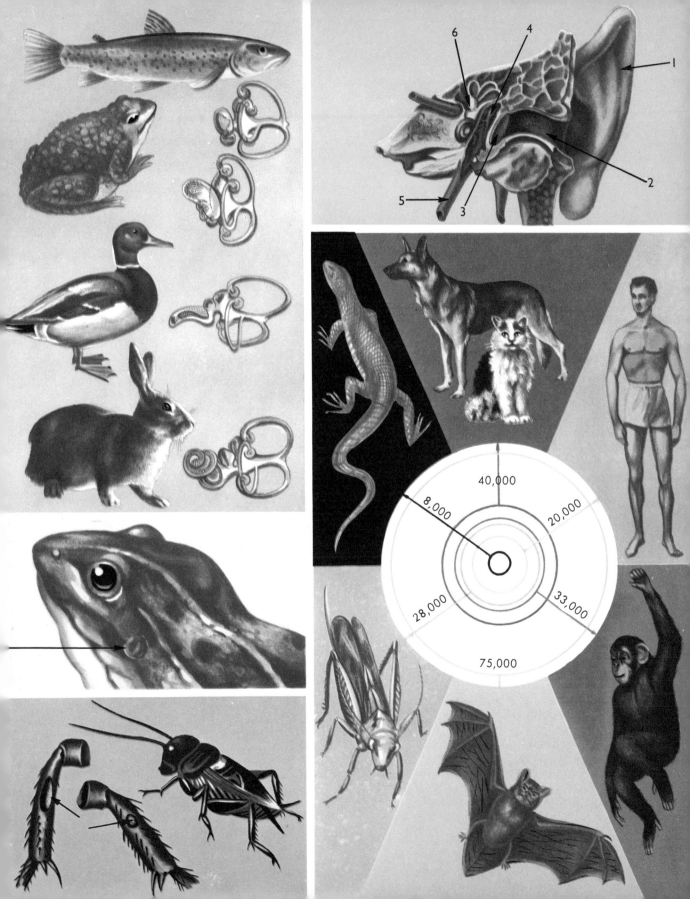

6   4   1

5   3   2

8,000   40,000   20,000

28,000   33,000

75,000

Sense of Touch and Sense of Balance

In a poem written after he went blind, John Milton lamented the fact that while we can feel things with every part of the body, our sense of sight is limited to two small and delicate eyes. Yet though the sense of touch is not localized like the senses of sight and hearing it is by no means a simple thing. By touch we can distinguish not only pressure, but also pain, heat, cold, wetness and dryness. We also know that some areas of the body—the tip of the tongue and the tips of the fingers, for instance—are more sensitive to touch than others.

Close to fur-covered or hair-covered parts of an animal's body, the nerves which carry tactile, or touch, sensations commonly receive particularly powerful stimuli. Our illustration shows a sea-elephant, with its imposing, bristly moustache. Below is a cross-section of the area where a single bristly hair sprouts from the skin. Around the hair-root are fine nerve fibers, sensitive to touch. If the tip of the hair is touched, the whole hair acts as a kind of lever, pressing against the nerve and powerfully stimulating it. A cat's whiskers act in a similar way. Even in complete darkness, the least contact with the tips of its whiskers serves to warn it of obstacles.

A fish possesses two different kinds of organs sensitive to pressure. Under a powerful magnifying glass and in a good light, much of its skin is seen to be covered with what look like tiny tower-shaped warts (lower part of fish picture). Each of these tiny "warts" is filled with a sticky fluid, and rests on a group of touch-sensitive cells. Changes in the pressure of the water around the fish produce changes in the pressure of liquid inside the "warts" and they, in turn, stimulate the sensitive cells nearby.

The top part of the picture shows a more complex sense organ. Along the fish's side is a line of small points. Each point is an opening leading into a long, thin canal filled with fluid. Changing water-pressure against the fish's side causes changes of pressure inside the canal, stimulating the nerves (shown red) beside it.

As a fish swims, it pushes the surrounding water aside. But if there is some solid object nearby, such as another fish, the water is not so easily pushed aside. Instead, it exerts extra pressure against the fish's side. The fish's delicate sense organs thus enable it to detect the presence of other fish, which may serve as its prey. They also enable it to notice changes in the strength and direction of currents.

A fish, living in buoyant water, is perhaps less sensitive to the pull of gravity than are land animals, which live in the far less buoyant medium of air. Yet it needs some way of distinguishing between up and down, otherwise it would have no sense of direction. It possesses an organ called a statocyst (bottom left) which serves this purpose. It works in a very similar way to the otoliths in our inner ear, mentioned on the last page. A tiny grain, moving about in the statocyst in the opposite direction to the fish's movements, comes into contact with different sensitive nerve ends, thus providing a sense of direction. It sometimes happens that a soft growth forms around the grain so that it cannot easily touch the nerve ends. The fish then behaves as if it were giddy, staggering about in the water with no sense of direction.

A shrimp has a similar organ for detecting the pull of gravity. But the shrimp can be tricked. If it is placed in a tank, with its antennae heavily sprinkled with iron filings, and if a magnet is then placed above the tank, the magnet pulls the shrimp more strongly than gravity does. The shrimp then swims upside down in the tank.

TOP: Why the sea-elephant's whiskers, in contact with nerve ends, are so sensitive (left). Pressure-sensitive organs in a fish (right). BOTTOM: The statocyst which gives a fish its sense of direction (left). When a shrimp cannot tell up from down (right).

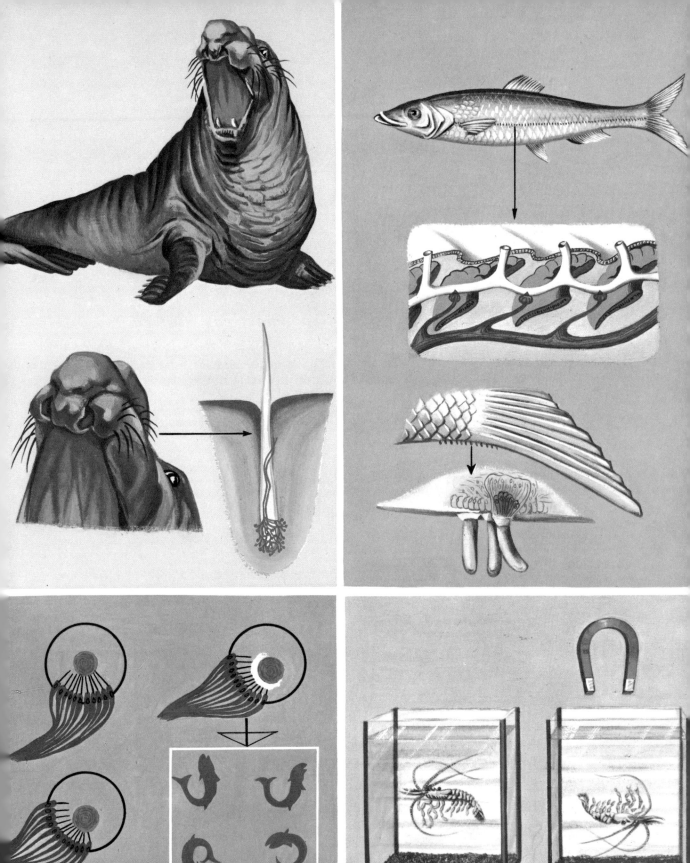

Nature's Songsters Sing with Reason

Biologists have a habit of questioning every-thing about nature. The habit springs from a well-founded belief that there is an explanation for everything in nature — for the existence of every organ, every organism and every phenom-enon. Some of us may think that the biologist is occasionally in danger of worrying too much about the reason and too little about the result. Yet, by patient observation and experiment, he is often able to get at information which adds to our own appreciation and understanding of the world around us.

Most of us would gratefully accept the singing of birds without troubling to ask why they sing. Not so biologists. They have been asking that question for many years. Because the bird-chorus reaches its climax during the mating season, they at first thought that the singing was mainly a device for attracting the opposite sex, or perhaps merely the adult bird's expression of the sheer joy of living. Many now believe, however, that birds' songs frequently sound a note of warning and defiance.

When a pair of birds begin nesting, they need a certain area around them where they can seek for food. It may well be that the song of the male bird carries a message of this sort: "I have staked my claim to this territory, and here I will build my nest; others may venture here only at their own peril." The warning is addressed not to all birds of every species, but only to male birds of the same species, and it is no idle threat. Bitter fights often occur between the holder of the terri-tory and would-be trespassers. Even doves, which we so often associate with olive branches and peace, have been known to fight almost to the death in such battles.

Bird-watchers have amassed quite a lot of evi-dence which tends to support this territorial theory of birdsong. After a time, trained observers can distinguish not only a species but also an individual bird by its singing. Such observers declare that in lonely woods (it is not so true in over-populated countryside) each individual thrush, blackbird or robin commonly stays in one limited area, right throughout spring, each keep-ing to its own well-defined territory. They say, too, that if a man can give a really good imitation of the song of the male yellowhammer, he can easily attract real yellowhammers. But *not*, as one might expect, the females. It is the male yellow-hammers which appear, perhaps to note what new territory is being staked out, perhaps to discover who is challenging their right to the area they already hold.

Yet even if this is an important reason for the singing of birds, it is certainly not the only one. Many birds carry on singing long after the mating season has ended, when the question of which territory belongs to which bird is no longer of such importance. Many sing, too, before the mating season properly begins. In that case the song doubtless does help to attract birds of the opposite sex, especially among species with drab plumage. But among birds of brilliant plumage the appeal is perhaps addressed more to the eye than to the ear.

Many kinds of sea birds make no claim to private territory. Gannets and gulls, for example, live and nest in huge colonies, sometimes crowd-ing closely together on a few narrow ledges of a single cliff, and leaving a nearby cliff quite empty of bird life. With no territorial claims to make or defend, such birds spend little energy on loud or prolonged cry or song.

The same is true of certain waterfowl which, while they do not form huge colonies, often live somewhat crowdedly in small lakes or ponds. Even in spring the stretch of water opposite would never produce the symphony of sound we hear in an April wood—only the occasional quacking of ducks and the sudden, sharp cry of moorhens.

The waterfowl here outnumber the perching birds from the surrounding trees. Yet it is the woodland birds, with territories to defend, whose cries are most frequent and prolonged.

Signals of Sound and Signals of Sight

We have seen that birds have characteristic songs which help them to recognize each other. But birds are only part of the community of living things dwelling in any given habitat. The community living on a heather-clad moor will be very different from that of a beach, a forest or a meadow. Each habitat has its own characteristic voices.

If you are a nature lover you could probably pick out the song of a blackbird or of a thrush from all the other singing in a wood. But stand in a meadow and try to separate the sounds that make up its quiet murmur. You can tell one species of insect from another by their sounds only if you are a specialist. Yet insects have their own distinctive sounds, and many of them communicate by sound, just as songbirds do.

Most insects, mammals and birds that live in one habitat spend their whole lives there. They are best adapted to finding food in surroundings of one particular kind, and would probably die if taken to a totally different region.

Seagulls are at home around coastal waters. Their raucous cries carry above the fiercest crashing of heavy breakers. But in winter they often wander inland, aided by the freedom that flight gives them, in search of more plentiful supplies of food. Yet the ghostly seagull cries you sometimes hear from a plowed field invariably bring their true dwelling place before your mind's eye: a rugged cliff, a shining pebble beach, a gleaming strip of sand.

Seagulls are wanderers. They can afford to be, for they are not at all particular about what food they eat. But we seldom see coral-billed oystercatchers far from tidal haunts, and we seldom hear their piping voices separated from the ceaseless rhythm of lapping waves. The scream of terns is another sea-sound we learn to link with dunes and marram grass where these birds nest in gigantic colonies.

The cries and songs of birds, the buzzing and stridulating of insects, are among the signals of sound by which animals communicate with one another. But nature communicates by sight as well as by sound. Terns, gulls, gannets, fulmars, and many other sea birds strike us as having very similar plumage. In fact, unless you are an expert you will find it very difficult to tell one species from another, especially at a distance. Yet if you observe them closely you will see that though they are all partly white, they are not *uniformly* white. Gannets have yellow heads, terns have black caps and different colored bills. The different distribution of color on wings, head or body distinguishes one species of sea bird from another. Thus the shine of white helps sea birds to keep within sight of their own colonies at a distance; the distinctive color patches enable them to distinguish one species from another nearer at hand.

We have all seen the bobbing white tail of a rabbit as it dashes down its burrow. That is a visual danger signal. When we see it *we* are usually the danger. Every habitat has animals that prey on others. Many of nature's sight and sound signals are warnings that a beast of prey is about. In dense jungles the white scut of a rabbit would be of little use. But the raucous voices of jungle birds and monkeys give ample warning to their neighbors that they have seen or scented a giant cat on the prowl. Hunters learn to follow the silent, stealthy movements of a tiger by the trail of jabbering and squawking that marks its passage through the jungle.

Nature's signals help animals to recognize a rival, to distinguish friend from foe, and to alert their neighbors to danger. Man has taken signals a step further. He uses the sounds of speech and the symbols of writing to communicate a wealth of ideas. Without speech and writing he could not have built up a civilized way of life.

ABOVE: The cries of gulls, terns and oystercatchers carry above the ceaseless sound of waves. BELOW: The screams of parrots and monkeys warn the jungle that a beast of prey is on the prowl.

Insects
and Mammals
Skilled in Navigation

"Once upon a time, when animals could talk ..." So some of our childhood fairy tales began. The storyteller assumed that, whatever they may have done in the distant past, animals certainly cannot talk now. True, no animals can indulge in true speech, as man does, but many of them can pass on simple information to one another. Modern naturalists have shown that some creatures can even convey quite complex messages to their fellows. This is especially true of animals which live in large social groups.

Perhaps the most striking example is the way that a honey bee tells other honey bees where they can find food. A worker bee buzzes by chance into a clump of flowers specially rich in nectar. It quickly homes back to the hive and does a dance. Rhythmically wriggling its body from side to side, it runs around the surface of the honeycomb in well-marked patterns—often in figures of eight—brushing past many hundred other worker bees. Soon others join the pattern of the dance.

It took many hours of patient observation for naturalists to learn just what these patterns mean. They found that the speed of the turns is related to the distance of the food from the hive. Thus 40 turns a minute indicate that the flower-patch is 100 yards away, 24 that it is 500 yards away. The figure of eight also tells in which direction the attractive flowers lie. If a straight line through the middle of the "8" points towards the sun, the flowers are in line with the sun. If it is at an angle to the sun, then the flowers are at the same angle to the sun. The only information the worker probably does not pass on by means of its dance is the type of food. It has no

need to. Its legs are already sticky with the nectar and pollen which bear a tell-tale scent.

In a sense we may say that these insects are accomplished navigators, using the sun as a means of finding or giving direction, and forming accurate estimates of distance. They certainly do not study navigation, as an airline pilot does. Either the skill exists, ready-made, in every member of a species, or else it is somehow acquired from older members of the species.

Bird migration raises a similar problem. How do carrier pigeons home many hundred miles over countries that neither they nor their parents have even seen? Naturalists have made experiments which seem to show that pigeons and certain migratory birds are hatched with some extra sense which acts as a kind of sextant for measuring the bearing of stars by night and the angle of the sun by day.

Skill in navigation is sometimes just as necessary over short journeys as over great distances. The midnight flitting of a bat around a village church is no less wonderful than the flight of the Arctic tern almost from pole to pole. Bats are not birds, but weak-eyed mammals which spend their days asleep, head-downwards. Yet at night they fly more skilfully than many a keen-eyed bird flies by day.

Only since man invented radar has he been able to understand the way these uncanny little mammals move around. Radar works by radio waves which pulse outwards, hit a solid object and return to register upon a screen. The bat finds its way in the dark by means of very short, high-pitched sound waves.

As it flies it gives out high-pitched squeaks. These echo back from any object nearby—from a church steeple to each strand of a criss-cross maze of threads strung across a pitchdark room. The bat's ears easily detect the high-pitched echoes which very few human ears can hear. Its brain translates the meaning of the echoes and its wings respond, helping it to avoid obstacles or to seize its prey.

ABOVE: The pattern of a bee's signalling dance. Direction tells which way flowers are, speed of dance tells their distance. BELOW: Bats sleep by day, steer by echoes in their flight by night.

Animal Skills that are Not Taught

When someone suddenly approaches a hand to your eye, you automatically close the eye. Your action is *reflex* — something which you did not have to learn. On the other hand you could not possibly have read this paragraph unless somebody had taught you to read. Your reading ability is an *acquired skill*—something you had to learn.

Most of our complex voluntary actions are the result of acquired skills. Our instinctive voluntary actions are, on the whole, simple ones. But in nature we find that many animals are born with the ability to perform quite complicated feats.

The leaf-cutter bees provide an amazing instance of innate behavior. The female digs a tunnel in a half-rotted wooden post. Then she bites off leaf segments from a rose bush or an apple tree. She lines the bottom of the tunnel with a round piece of leaf and the sides with oblong pieces. She fills the bottom of the cup with pollen and nectar, and lays an egg in it. Then she covers it with another round piece of leaf, adds more pollen and nectar, lays another egg and covers that too. She goes on until the tunnel is full. Then she flies off and leaves the eggs to hatch into grubs. They have a plentiful supply of food, and in time they turn into bees themselves. Those which are females will later follow all the nest-making actions of their mother. Yet they have never seen her and could not possibly have learned from her.

Instinct plays its part even in the underwater world. The bitterling's behavior is no less amazing than the leaf-cutter bee's. In spring, this small, drab relation of the common carp undergoes certain changes. The silver-green male begins to glow with a reddened belly and ruddy fins.

The female does not change color, but she grows a long ovipositor, or egg-laying tube.

The male and female bitterling swim close to a freshwater mussel lodged at the bottom of their pond. The female inserts her ovipositor into the mussel's gill slits and lays her eggs inside. The male fertilizes the eggs with milt which floats after the eggs into their incredible nursery. Inside the mussel shell the eggs develop safely, secure from the many foes which throng the watery world outside. At last they hatch. The young fish swim freely away and, in time, repeat the miraculous performance which they have never learned.

The story has a sequel. The mussel's young are hatched bearing a long, sticky filament. With this they cling to any passing fish to be carried to less crowded feeding grounds. Very often the fish which provides the "lift" is a bitterling. The story has come full circle!

We may not be familiar with leaf-cutter bees and bitterlings, but we have all seen a bird's nest and marvelled at the way it is made. True, we build impressive homes of our own, but human beings have to learn their building skills. A bird builds by instinct. Yet naturalists have shown that they use experience to supplement instinct. Often a first-year's nest is in a bad place. Beside a well-worn woodland path for instance, sky-blue thrush eggs in a pale mud cup attract attention, and the nest may be robbed. But the bird learns from this. Next year it builds out of sight, as well as out of wind and rain.

By instinct and experience each species adapts its nests to the sites available within its habitat. Thus in the desert lands in the southwest of the United States, roadrunners—strange, lanky birds related to the cuckoo—build not on open sandy ground, but among the spiteful prickles of cactus plants. *How* the roadrunner build its nest is a matter of instinct. *Where* it builds is probably something it has learned.

ABOVE: Leaf-cutter bee and nest. LEFT: A bitterling lays eggs inside a mussel. RIGHT: A roadrunner nesting in a cactus plant.

The Wonder of a Spider's Web

A spider's web is another example of innate behavior. Instinctively a spider spins its craftsmanlike fly-trap that combines the mesh of a fisherman's net with the stickiness of a fly-paper. Instinctively she begins spinning early in the morning, before the insects which fly by day are on the wing. In forty minutes she has created a work of art.

The left-hand illustrations show some of the stages in the construction of a garden spider's web. First the spider reconnoiters the twigs and leaves which she will make the foundations of her fortress. When she has chosen a firm twig (A), she glues a silken thread on to it and drops down from the thread. The lightest breeze will help her to swing several inches across a chasm to the next twig (B). Once the spider has made her slender rope bridge she runs to and fro across it, multiplying its silk strands, for this is her foundation stone. But unlike man's buildings, hers will grow downwards.

From the middle of the bridge A to B, she drops a new line from C to D. As the diagrams show, this simple shape soon becomes more complex. Threads F and E respectively connect points D A and D B. Then another bridge, from G to H, is built parallel to the first. Once the outer framework is ready, the spider runs to the middle of the web and from there she spins "spokes" in all directions. Finally she links the spokes with a spiral thread, beginning in the center and working outwards.

Now that her trap is laid, the spider awaits her unwilling guests in the middle of her web. She hangs head downwards, her eight legs stretched out, ready to leap into action at a moment's notice. As well as being a trap, her web also acts as a system of telegraph lines. As soon as a fly gets caught in a corner, its struggles vibrate the "spokes" running to the center and so inform the spider where it is.

The spider leaps upon her victim and bites it to reduce its struggles. Then she spins threads around it, turning it over and over as we might wrap up a parcel. Soon the hapless fly looks like a cocoon.

The threads which imprison a fly are different from those the spider spins to build her web. She can produce altogether four different kinds of substance from the spinneret glands at the hindpart of her body: first, the dry threads which make the "spokes" of her web; second, the sticky thread which spirals outwards and holds the structure together; third, the silk that binds up her victim; fourth, the yellow silk with which she spins a covering around her own eggs. This yellow silk probably contains some sort of nourishment for the baby spiders when they hatch.

Spiders can secrete web-building substances only when they have had a square meal, and nature has ensured that these substances are not wasted by the building of webs in stormy weather. Instinctively spiders seem to foretell the weather. If it is unsettled and there is a chance of a web being blown away, they conserve their silk until better conditions set in.

The garden spider's web we have described is the sort with which most of us are familiar. But there are many species of spider and many types of web. The right-hand illustrations show four of them. The top picture illustrates a web rather like a bird-catcher's net. The spider sits on a stout thread outside the main web. If an insect falls into the web, she pulls her thread and brings the web down to tangle around it. The second picture shows a trap which works like a wartime balloon barrage. Insects collide with the "cables" above the web, and fall to their doom. Yet other spiders build webs parallel to the ground, and some (bottom picture) create a dome which rivals any man-made work of architecture.

LEFT: A garden spider and four stages in the making of her web. RIGHT: Four kinds of web spun by spiders of different species.

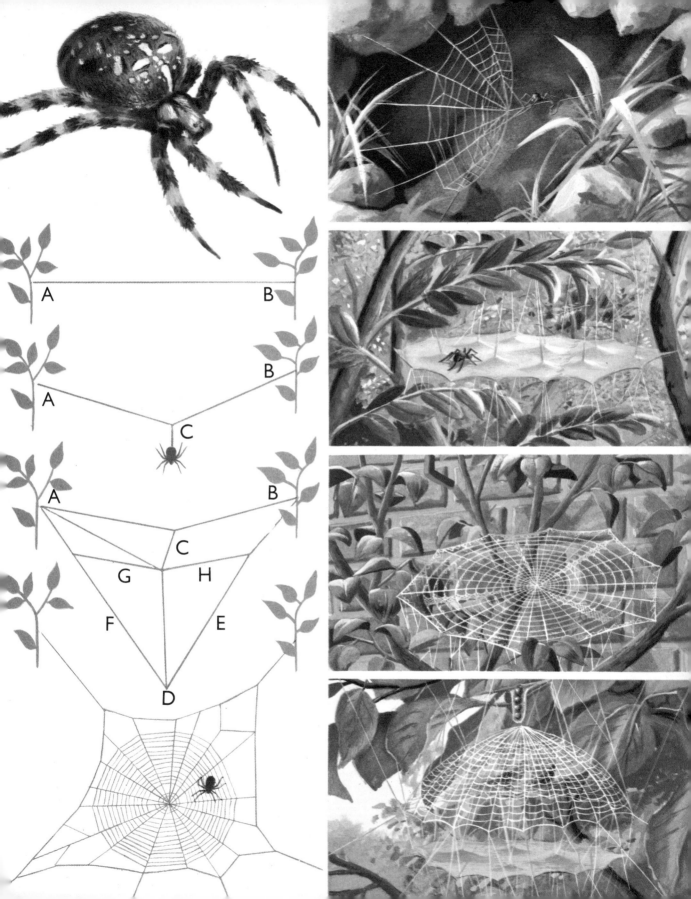

Glands - the Body's Chemical Factories

Many spiders can inflict a poisonous bite which enables them to stupefy or even to kill their prey. They secrete the poison with the aid of glands. Glands consist of specialized cells, or groups of cells, valuable to men and animals for the substances that they produce. They can be likened to tiny factories, producing chemicals. We have sweat glands, glands to produce saliva, glands to produce digestive juices, and many others, all working inside the body to keep its machinery running efficiently.

Plants also have glands which secrete complicated chemical substances. Thus insect-eating plants have glands to produce digestive juices, some trees have glands which produce the latex from which rubber is made, and many flowers possess glands which isolate their quickly-evaporating oils.

Glandular cells often multiply to form cell colonies — colonies of visible and even appreciable size. Such a cell colony makes up one gland. The skin of frogs and salamanders contains many glandular cells busy secreting the slime which keeps the outer surface of these creatures moist. As these cells become full they must expand. But they cannot expand sideways because the surrounding body cells are not easily compressed. Instead they develop downwards and the concentration of single-cell glands make up one multi-cell gland.

Glands may be classified into two main groups. The exocrine glands discharge their secretions through an opening on to a surface. The endocrine glands pour their secretions directly into the blood. We shall see something of the endocrine glands on the next page, but here we are concerned only with exocrine glands.

In man these exocrine glands include not only the sweat glands and tear glands which connect with the outer surface of the body, but also the many different glands which pour juices on to the internal surface of the digestive tract.

Many animals have exocrine glands which provide them with a means of defense or attack. We have mentioned the poison glands of some spiders. Few spiders can pierce human skin, but the sting of a tropical scorpion is something to be reckoned with. It can cause serious illness to adults and may even prove fatal to children.

A scorpion's hook-shaped sting grows from the tip of its tail. When it is thrust forward into the victim's body, the pressure forces poison from a gland into the puncture the sting has made. A snake-bite works in a similar way. The pressure of the snake's fangs against its victim forces poison from a sac at the root of the fang. The poison flows down the snake's hollow or grooved tooth into the wound. The mechanism is as effective as any hypodermic syringe.

Skunks are handsome creatures whose furry skins are held in high repute. But skunks have another kind of reputation too. When they are annoyed, they emit a frightful odor from two glands at the back of the body which secrete an oily yellow liquid. By contracting muscles near these glands the skunk can aim this offensive liquid accurately at a distance of several yards. The skunk's weapon could be compared to an efficient but highly unpleasant scent-spray. No wonder that, with such a weapon, they are such fearless creatures.

Not all animal gland-secretions are offensive to man. For centuries scent manufacturers used natural musk. One prized source of it was the musk deer, rather like the roebuck. The male deer secretes musk in a kind of pocket beneath its stomach. Within this pocket tiny glands produce the scent which is released through two small openings when the pocket is full. Nature's musk glands still fulfill the several functions for which they evolved. They leave a scent trail which marks out the territory of the animal that bears them. They also help members of the same species to recognize the presence of their fellows at a great distance.

ABOVE: Tarantula spider, scorpion, venomous snake — animals which use glands as weapons of attack. LEFT: The skunk's glands provide an effective weapon of defense. RIGHT: The musk deer.

Ductless Glands
and Health

Most mammals, man included, possess endocrine, or ductless, glands. These glands do not pour their secretions on to the surface of the body, or on to the surface of some organ of the body, but empty their chemical products directly into the bloodstream. We call the products of these glands hormones. Whatever part of the body these glands may be in, their hormones influence the whole body, for the bloodstream carries them to all its parts.

One of the leading pioneers of endocrinology (the study of ductless glands) was the great French physiologist Claude Bernard (1813-78). Thanks largely to his thorough study of the pancreas doctors have learned the causes and cures of certain puzzling illnesses.

For many centuries anatomists knew of an organ behind the stomach, some six inches long and two to two-and-a-half inches wide. But they certainly did not know it was a gland, and they had no idea what an important part it plays in the workings of our body. They thought it was simply made up of flesh, so they called it the "pancreas", from two Greek words meaning all flesh.

Today we know that the pancreas consists mainly of little groups of gland cells linked to the duodenum by an extremely intricate system. Our illustration (top right) shows the pancreas. The circular diagram below shows a magnified section through it. Such a magnified view helps us to understand just what the pancreas really does.

Most of its gland cells pour out juices which aid digestion. But set in the middle of the pancreatic tissue are small islands of different cells, known as the islets of Langerhans. These produce a secretion called insulin, from the Latin *insulae*, islands, and this substance flows directly into the bloodstream. It reaches all parts of the body and controls the body's use of sugar.

What happens when things go wrong with the pancreas? If the islets of Langerhans stop working properly the sugar in our blood increases and we become ill with the disease called diabetes mellitus. Scientists have shown that diabetes, once a most serious illness, frequently arises because of the lack of minute amounts of the hormone insulin from these vitally important gland cells.

Once it was proved that insulin controls the amount of sugar in the blood, scientists set about finding artificial ways of giving it to people suffering from diabetes. Today whole factories are devoted to the production of insulin from the pancreatic glands of animals. One such factory is shown opposite. Today the insulin industry is the lifeline of many thousands of diabetics.

Most people suffering from the disease can now live a normal life by giving themselves insulin injections. A few minutes after the hormone enters their bloodstream it begins to cut down the excess sugar content. Thanks to insulin, doctors can even save people who have gone into a diabetic coma.

Unfortunately insulin injections are only potent for a few hours. They must be constantly repeated. Scientists have not yet built factories which can provide a service as efficient as that given by the islets of Langerhans.

But research still goes on. On December 10th, 1958, Dr. Frederick Sanger became the fourth person to be awarded the Nobel Prize for Chemistry in connection with insulin research. Dr. Sanger was the first man to find out the precise composition of a molecule of insulin. Of the twenty-four known amino acid "beads", an insulin molecule contains seventeen. You can imagine how much work must have gone into establishing what its pattern is.

This new knowledge not only gave scientists a deeper understanding of how insulin works; it is now possible to produce this substance synthetically instead of extracting it from the pancreas of animals.

TOP: Claude Bernard and the pancreas he studied. CENTER: Man-made insulin factory and magnified section of pancreas showing the islets of Langerhans, nature's insulin factory. BELOW: Structure of insulin molecule and its discoverer, Dr. Frederick Sanger.

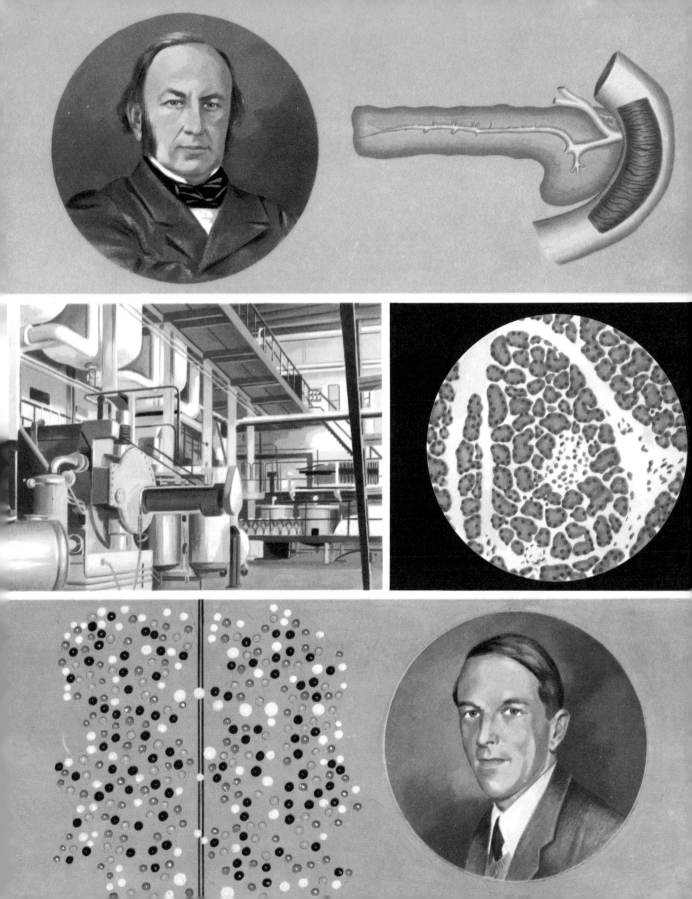

Glands and Growth

The word hormone comes from a Greek word meaning to stimulate, and insulin is only one of many different hormones which course around in the bloodstream stimulating various body organs into activity. The study of hormones is still comparatively new, but what we have already learned about them supplies the answers to many age-old riddles.

People far larger or far smaller than the average have always aroused curiosity. But for many years giants and dwarfs were simply regarded as themes for strange tales such as *Gulliver's Travels*. Great differences in the sizes of human beings are now the subject of serious research. Doctors now know that they result from an excess or a lack of hormones produced by the pituitary, a ductless gland no bigger than a pea at the base of the brain. It is odd to think that minute quantities of a single hormone can determine the size and shape to which we grow. Yet this is so.

Too much secretion from the pituitary during youth results in the long bones of the body continuing to grow when they should have stopped. Thus there are records of seventeen-year-old giants eight feet tall. A deficiency of the pituitary's growth-hormone in childhood may result in growth stopping far too soon. Thus there are "full-grown" dwarfs less than three feet tall.

Giants and dwarfs are rare. But slight variations in the activity of the pituitary gland give rise to the variety of fat, thin, tall and short people we see every day of our lives. Our pictures of the tall, lean poet Dante, the short, plump composer Bach, and that mythical idea of athletic manhood, Hercules, are typical of three such widely different types.

Yet hormones are not responsible for all the differences of human size. A visit to the armory of a museum might lead you to believe that medieval knights were deficient in hormones, because their armor would certainly not fit a man of average size today. But one reason for this difference may be in diet, not hormones. The men of the Middle Ages were capable of growing to the same height as the men of today, but nobles lived largely on badly balanced meaty diets.

Hormones play an important part in the life of other animals beside man. Biologists have discovered, for instance, that hormones control the way in which certain insects renew their skins. They have shown that a woodlouse can live for months without a head; but in that unenviable condition it can no longer renew its outer skin. Yet if blood from an unmutilated woodlouse is introduced into the body of the headless one, it soon sets to work and renews old skin tissues. There is a gland in the woodlouse's head which produces a hormone that controls the workings of its skin-forming cells.

If you tie a thread around the middle of a caterpillar a few days before it turns into a chrysalis, blood cannot circulate freely between the front and the rear parts of the body. It then happens that only the fore-part turns into a chrysalis. The reason lies in hormones secreted in the fore-part of the caterpillar's body. Scientists have discovered the gland which produces them. When just a tiny piece of it is transplanted into the rear part of the half-chrysalis-half-caterpillar, both ends become a chrysalis in the normal way, in spite of the thread.

Plants, too, have glands which produce substances that control how they grow and how they produce their flowers. Some of these substances have amazing effects on animals. One such substance has been extracted from the autumn crocus and injected into rabbits. Rabbits treated in this way grew to three times normal size, but they were not able to raise litters of their own. So the time has not yet come when we may expect to breed pigs as big as elephants to help solve the world's food problem.

TOP LEFT: Gulliver in Lilliput: TOP RIGHT: Modern man against almost dwarfish medieval armor. CENTER: (A) Dante, (B) Bach, (C) Hercules. BOTTOM LEFT: Caterpillar-chrysalis. BOTTOM RIGHT: Autumn crocus hormone produces giant rabbit.

B

C

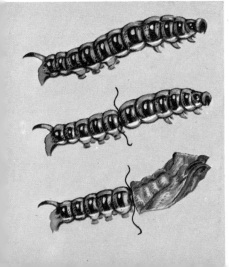

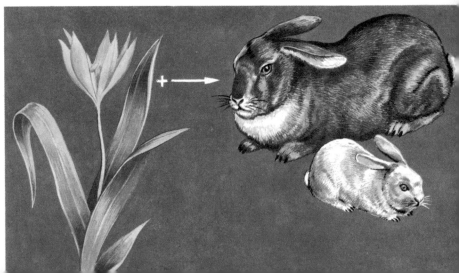

Hormones and Human Development

So far we have spotlighted only one or two of the endocrine glands whose hormones regulate the workings of our bodies. There are at least eight, though we cannot say with absolute certainty exactly what tasks each performs. These glands are the pineal, pituitary, thyroid, parathyroids, thymus, islets of Langerhans, adrenals and the interstitial cells of the sex glands. You can see them mapped and numbered on the opposite page.

The pineal gland (1) is something of a puzzle. We know that eons ago, in the long story of evolution, it was a sort of primitive eye in many animals. In its present position inside the human head, it may possibly help to control our growth and the way we reach maturity as men and women.

The pituitary gland (2) at the base of the skull and linked with the brain, is really the commander of the whole army of endocrine glands. The front part secretes at least six hormones. Most of them act as dispatch riders, carrying commands to the body's other ductless glands. One is the growth-hormone whose effects we have already seen. The rear part of the pituitary produces a hormone which affects certain internal muscles.

The thyroid gland (4) which lies near the Adam's apple, is the body's chief iodine depot. People whose thyroid gland secretes too much iodine-rich hormone become overactive. They get thin, lose weight, perspire freely and sometimes develop dilated, staring eyes. People whose thyroid secretes too little become sluggish. They get fat, their skin becomes dry and their pulse rate and body temperature drop.

Behind the thyroid lie the parathyroids (3). These small glands secrete a hormone which controls the body's supply of calcium and the content of phosphorus in bones and blood. People whose parathyroids are not working properly may develop twitching muscles and convulsions, but doctors can now prevent this by giving parathyroid hormone extract.

Roughly level with the top of the breastbone is the thymus (5), something of a mystery gland. By the time we reach adolescence, its work seems to be accomplished, for it then shrinks into a fatty lump. Scientists have still to isolate and analyze the hormones produced in the thymus; but they are almost sure that these hormones help to control our early growth.

We have already seen how the islets of Langerhans, situated in the pancreas (6), keep our body sugar at its proper level. Close to the pancreas are the adrenal glands (7), attached to both kidneys. Each consists of an inner and an outer part. The outer part secretes hormones which regulate the way we use and store up the foods we eat and the water we drink. The inner part secretes adrenalin, the hormone which comes into action most powerfully when we are faced with an emergency and must either fight or flee. One part of adrenalin to many million parts of blood is all we need. Yet without that infinitesimal amount we could not lead a normal life.

Special cells within the sex glands (8a and 8b) secrete the hormones which determine that if you are a boy you will probably want to be out and about in search of adventure while if you are a girl you will want to play quieter games. In later life these hormones help to determine other sex differences: to make men bearded and to control the masculine way their muscles develop; in women, to produce long hair, beardless chins and a slighter, characteristically feminine physique.

Some women, anxious to keep their feminine figures, take slimming diets which include synthetic hormones. But as we have seen, a little hormone can go a very long way. Hormones as slimming treatment may be very dangerous unless taken under medical supervision.

Blue silhouettes map the "geography" of eight endocrine glands. Top pictures show (left) effect of too-active and (right) too-inactive growth-glands. Cells within the sex glands (8a and 8b) influence typical differences of behavior and appearance between boys and girls, men and women.

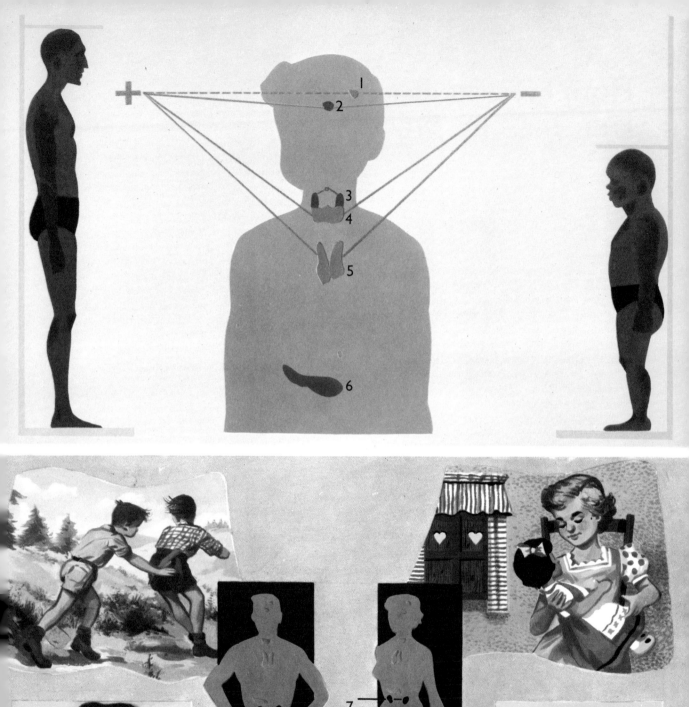
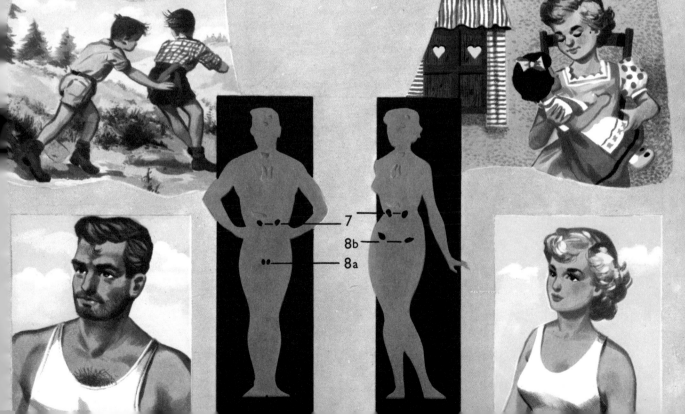

How Flowers, Roots and Tendrils Move

Animals and plants both possess hormones to keep their "machinery" working. But movement, the most notable feature of machinery, is more characteristic of animals than of plants. Even so, many plants can and do move, to a limited extent.

Biologists have made experiments to study how they do so. With cameras which take one photograph every few minutes and with projectors which show those photographs in rapid succession on a screen, they can present the life cycle of a plant in a five-minute film. The plant's movements, far too slow for the eye to take in, then spring to life and are easy to follow.

Sunlight seems to be the most compelling outside influence on plant movement. This is easy to understand when we remember that green leaves are chemical factories depending on sunlight for their energy. But the example of movement with which most of us are familiar is provided not by leaves but by a flower — the sunflower, whose great disc follows the sun's course round the heavens as if magnetized by the sun's rays. At night the flower droops downwards, but as the sun rises, it slowly faces eastwards. As the sun climbs the sky, the sunflower not only changes direction but also lifts upwards to keep face to face with it. Then, in the afternoon, it follows the westward path of the sun, gradually drooping as the sun lowers.

When such an outside stimulus makes a plant move, scientists call the movement a tropism. The Greek word for sun is *helios,* and movements produced by sunlight are called heliotropic. Movements towards the sunlight are described as positive heliotropism, those away from it as negative heliotropism. Often the word phototropism, meaning light movement, is used instead.

In general, only those parts of a plant which grow above ground are phototropic. Yet biologists have proved that the newly-formed roots of growing plants have the property of negative phototropism. If exposed to light, they turn away from it. Experiments with adult plant roots show that they make no discernible movement either way in response to light.

Quite different influences determine the way in which mature roots move beneath the soil. Certain simple experiments help to show what these influences are and how they work. A normal plant stem grows upright out of a flower pot, while the roots grow straight down (top right). When the flower pot is laid on its side the plant gradually moves. Its stem bends upwards and its roots down. It seems, then, that the roots — like the water they must find — obey the law of gravity and are drawn towards the earth's center. Biologists call this kind of plant behavior geotropism, or earth-movement. We see it in trees which grow on a slope. Their trunks do not grow at right angles to the slope, but point vertically upward. Their roots point vertically downward.

Sunlight and gravity are but two stimuli to which plants respond. A third is touch. Climbing plants like vines and peas react to objects which they touch in their upward growth. Scientists call this reaction haptotropism, after the Greek *haptein,* meaning to touch. Such plants do not aim deliberately at their supports. Their tendrils swing blindly and very slowly round and round until they touch something. Then they continue to twine slowly around it, making the plant secure.

One might be tempted to ask how it is that plants can move without muscles. The answer is that, in general, they do not move in the same kind of way as animals do. All the tropisms described above are not free movements, but examples of specialized forms of growth. But there are plant movements of other kinds, too. In some, varying tensions in the vegetable tissues cause stretching and contracting. Thus the leaves of insect-eating plants clamp shut on their prey at an amazing speed. Some plants, too, such as the poppy and the sweet pea, have mechanisms which fire their ripe seeds a considerable distance.

From dawn to sunset, the sunflower points towards the sun. Even if they have to change position to do so, roots point downwards. Vine tendrils move round and grip their supports.

Rotifers - the Wheel-bearing Worms

On page 21 we saw some of the multitude of single-cell organisms which may be found in just a single drop of pond-water. There are also many multi-cell creatures so small that they are quite at ease within the restricted confines of a drop of water. Most of them are tiny masterpieces of nature's craftsmanship which the most skilled jeweler could never hope to imitate.

Among the most interesting are the rotifera, or wheel-bearers. Naturalists classify them among the *vermes,* or worm-like animals, though most laymen would find it difficult to see much resemblance between them and, say, earthworms or lug-worms. Most of them are no bigger than the average single-cell water creature, and can be seen only with the help of a powerful microscope. At the front of their bodies they have a "wheel"—a rotating band surrounded with very fine hairs—which in most species can be withdrawn under a kind of scaly skin. The hairs, moving at the rate of some twenty beats a second, set up currents which draw food-particles towards the rotifer's stomach, where they are ground up by minute horny projections. The whole "wheel" also serves as a kind of steering apparatus during swimming. It may help, too, in propelling the rotifer through the water; but many of these creatures also possess a single hooked foot which they can use either for swimming or for clinging to things. Some of them, indeed, cling to plants and other objects for long periods, living as parasites.

Though they prefer a fresh water home, they can also live in rock crevices or among damp moss. In surroundings of that kind, they are sometimes faced with conditions of drought or famine. When that happens, they shrivel up (1) and appear to be lifeless. Yet in that shriveled and dried-up state they can survive for quite long periods, successfully withstanding conditions of great heat or intense cold.

Certain species of rotifera (2a) live in small brownish-colored tubes built up from tiny grains of waste matter which have passed through their own bodies. This is true only of the female. The male (2b), which is far smaller, remains always a free-swimming animal.

In some of these strange wheel-bearing worms (3) the "wheel" does not serve the same purpose as in their relations. In the long course of evolution it has become a set of five minute cones, each tipped with a tuft of long, fine threads. The Latin name for these creatures, *Floscularia ornata,* means "carrying small ornamental flowers". The transformed "wheel" does indeed seem to be more ornamental than useful, for the threads do not move. The creature relies on tiny lashes in another part of its body to set up food-carrying currents. These beautiful "flower-carriers", with their lower part surrounded by a fine, sticky membrane, live attached to water plants.

The creatures shown at the left and bottom of the picture (4 and 5) are not rotifers. They belong to another category of animals called polyzoa or bryozoa, most of which live together in large colonies. Though each individual is very small, a whole colony, living on a plant or a piece of wood, may measure a foot or more in length. Most of these creatures live in stagnant fresh-water, usually where it is clear but well shaded. They choose mollusks and stones, as well as plants and wood, as the sites of their colonies.

One of the remarkable things about the polyzoa is that they multiply during summer by means of fertilized eggs; but in late autumn, before the whole colony dies, they produce minute and very hardy reproductive bodies called statoblasts, in the same kind of way as certain plants produce seeds. These statoblasts preserve life throughout the cold winter months, and in spring they give rise to new animals, ready to found new colonies.

A few of the tiny multi-cell creatures which may live in a drop of water. Numbers 1, 2a, 2b and 3 are rotifera; 4 and 5 are polyzoa.

Monster of Myth, Monster in Miniature

According to Greek mythology, Hercules was the mighty son of Jupiter, father of the gods. Stories of Hercules could not well be straightforward, plausible tales of great physical strength. They had to have a supernatural or downright impossible element about them. So one of the creatures in the Hercules myths was a thoroughly impossible beast — the many-headed hydra. Every time one of its heads was cut off, a new one immediately grew in its place. Finally Hercules had to kill it with a brazen club.

The hydra of mythology was just about as impossible an animal as man could imagine. Yet creatures just as remarkable really do exist in great numbers. They are miniature creatures living in ponds and, appropriately enough, they bear the name of hydra. They are seldom as much as half an inch long, and in a pond they can easily hide from view under quite small water plants. But put a little of the pond-water in a test-tube, with only a few water plants, and soon you may see a hydra thrusting out its long tentacles. You might well mistake the hydra itself for a small plant until you noticed how the tentacles writhe and twist like tiny serpents.

The fresh-water hydra is only a very small and humble member of the animal kingdom, consisting of little more than a stomach and eight tentacles. Its bulky central part, containing the stomach, is merely a small sac, not unlike the finger of a tiny glove; one end is closed while the other is open like a miniature mouth. But the eight tentacles, growing like a circle of fine petals from the central sac, are among the most remarkable "arms" possessed by any creature.

They are prehensile organs — organs adapted to grasping, seizing, holding on. Seen under a microscope, each appears to be pitted with many tiny holes. When the hydra is at rest they hang down in the water like harmless threads (D), but when any minute fresh water shellfish ventures near, they flash out (A), seize it, and carry it to the hydra's mouth. Layers of cells inside the hydra's stomach pour out fluids which quickly cover the prey and help to digest it. The tentacles serve other purposes, too. They can be made shorter and thicker (C), and in that form they enable the hydra to move about on the slippery surface of water plants (B).

Yet perhaps the most remarkable thing about these tentacles is that if they are cut off they very quickly grow again, like the heads of the hydra in the myth. Indeed, the tiny hydra of the pond is every bit as tough as its namesake was alleged to be. It can be turned inside out, like an empty sack, and still live. It can be cut up into several bits and some will produce the whole organism again. Not only does the hydra excel at preserving its own individual life. It also has unusual ways of passing life on. An individual hydra may produce both eggs, near the rear of its body, and male cells, near its tentacles, to fertilize them. In addition, it may also develop a kind of bud, as a plant does. This bud then grows into a new hydra which, when it is big enough, breaks away and lives a separate life.

If we take a closer look at how the hydra catches its prey, we shall see that it is also an accomplished hunter with very formidable weapons. Its fast-moving, twining tentacles can play the part of a lasso. Their tips, sharply pointed, can pierce the fine shells of fresh water crustaceans just as a harpoon pierces the skin and blubber of a whale. Once they have punctured their prey, the deadly tentacles release poison from glands which paralyze it. So, besides weapons like lasso and harpoon, its armory also includes one like the Red Indian's blow-pipe and poisoned darts.

The hydra of the myth and the real-life hydra. The real hydra carries weapons comparable with those in the bottom pictures, and can grow new tentacles when old ones are cut off.

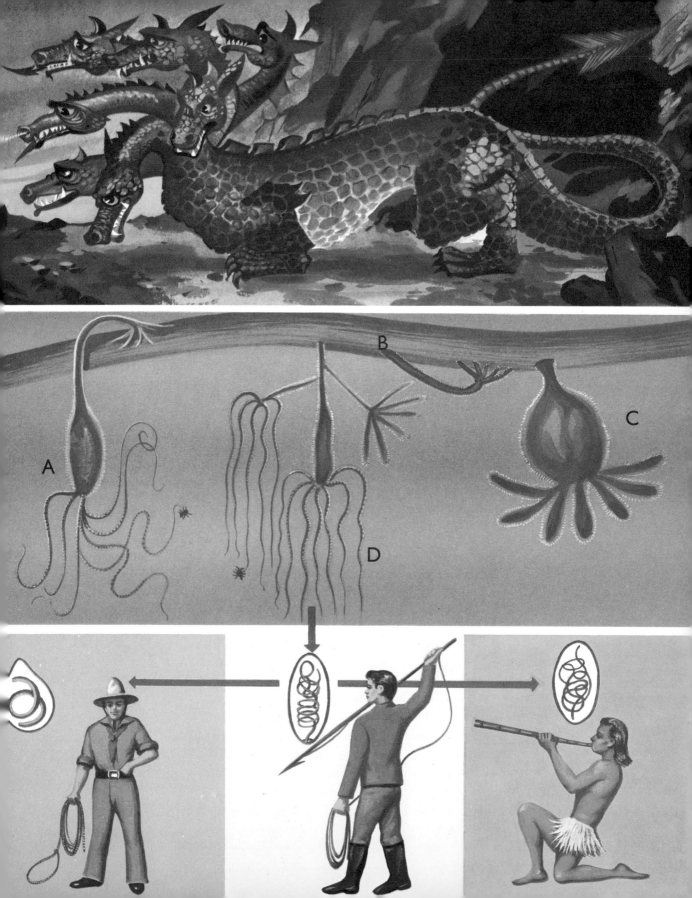

The Living Community of Meadow Lands

A meadow, a prairie, or a stretch of grazing land is not just an area of soil covered by a large number of closely-packed grass-stems. It is a close-knit community of many different plants and many different forms of animal life, all in some way or another dependent on each other.

Most numerous and most important, of course, are the grassy plants themselves — plants which must be able to grow and grow again in spite of repeated mowings. In cultivated fields most of the plants must be able to reproduce vegetatively— that is, from bulbs, corms, tubers or wide-spreading roots from which complete new plants can grow. The reason is that by the time the first hay-harvest comes around, and their stems are cut down, their seeds are not yet ripe.

The grasses and grass-like plants of the meadows form a rich and varied part of the vegetable kingdom. Seven of them are shown in the top picture. As you may well imagine, the names which country people give them vary from one county to another, and sometimes even from one village to the next. So we here give their botanical names, which all naturalists throughout the world use and understand, but we also give a rough translation of those names. They are 1 *Lolium temulentum* (drunken tares); 2 *Dactylis glomerata* (clustered fingers); 3 *Eriophorum vaginatum* (sheathed cotton-bearer); 4 *Alopecurus pratensis* (meadow foxtail); 5 *Phleum pratense* (meadow rush); 6 *Cynosurus cristatus* (crested dog's tail); 7 and 8 *Anthoxanthum odoratum* (scented tawny flower). The two pictures of the last-named plant help to show how some herbaceous plants alter their shape at a certain stage of growth.

The right-hand side of the picture shows some of the plants other than grasses which grow in a meadow: 1 the thistle; 2 a kind of knapweed; 3 the herb Robert; 4 the lesser centaury; 5 the daisy.

In bygone times some of them, particularly the centaury, were believed to have very valuable medicinal properties.

The left-hand side of the picture shows some of the typical animal life of the grasslands of Britain and many parts of northwest Europe: 1 and 3 butterflies; 2 earthworm; 4 ant; 5 centipede; 6 beetle; 7 grasshopper; 8 cricket; 9 mole; 10 shrewmouse.

Meadows flourish well almost anywhere where there is relatively good soil and adequate humidity, but most herbaceous plants do not stand up well to drought conditions. Their leaves have too big a surface area and they are too thin-skinned. In grasslands, which in summer may be exposed to the full glare of the sun throughout the day, they gain some protection and shelter from each other, for they grow close together and are commonly much of the same height.

Meadowlands are also fully exposed to the winds, and they thus have a long period of winter rest. In climates like that of England, vegetation does not resume growth much before mid-April. Yet in June the first hay-harvest is reaped. However, the grasses soon develop new shoots and other plants quickly come into flower, and by August the meadow is again a mass of delicate colors. Often, in August, there is a second harvest which results in the cutting down of all this new vegetation, leaving the ground sparsely covered once more.

Most meadowland plants spring up anew each year. They can be classified into three groups:

(1) Grasses which seed before the hay-harvest and which start growing as soon as circumstances permit;

(2) Plants with tubers or rhizomes, in which the parts above ground dry up naturally before the June hay-harvest;

(3) Plants which start to grow well before the first mowing begins.

By June the greater part of the grasses are in flower and their stems toss to and fro at the bidding of the wind.

CENTER: The living community of a meadow. TOP: Various herbaceous plants. RIGHT: Other plants of European meadows. LEFT: Animals of the grasslands.

The Natural
Balance of Life

All, or almost all, the plants and animals which go to make up the living community of a meadow make some contribution to the welfare of the others. Flowers, for instance, provide insects with nectar, while insects help to pollinate the flowers. Plants provide food for earthworms, while earthworms aerate the soil for plants. Mammals may nibble plant-shoots, but their droppings enrich the soil and promote vigorous plant growth.

Partnerships of a similar kind exist in all natural habitats. If we take a few fishes from a pond and place them in a bowl of water we can, no doubt, say that they are still in their natural element. But that is not to say they are still as well-off. Before long they will begin rising to the surface for air. After a few days, at most, the water will become cloudy and will have an unpleasant smell. If at that stage we fail to change it, the fishes will very soon die.

In a small bowl of water, fishes soon use up the available oxygen and it is not easily replaced. The waste matter from their bodies soon fouls the water, and there is no easy way of cleansing it. But in a pond, water plants are constantly replenishing the supply of oxygen; bacteria are constantly breaking down waste animal matter and converting it into substances which plants can absorb. All the inhabitants of the pond help each other. That is why the expert who keeps an aquarium makes sure that it contains a wide variety of plants and water animals. He tries, on a small scale, to re-create the natural balance of a pond.

One aspect of this natural balance in nature is fairly easy to understand. In natural communities, just as in human communities, there are producers and consumers. Again, just as in human communities, it is impossible to draw a sharp line between those who produce and those who consume. In every town there are tailors who produce clothes and consume food; there are also bakers and millers who are producers of food and consumers of clothes. Similarly in a pond there are plants which consume carbon dioxide and produce food and oxygen, and there are animals which consume food and oxygen and produce carbon dioxide.

What is more difficult to understand is how nature keeps the balance so delicately adjusted. If the plants spread too fast, they would eventually cover the whole surface of the water, making it hard for the fishes to breathe. If every fish's egg developed into an adult fish, there would be a severe shortage of food. If all the plants died out the water might soon be without enough oxygen for the fishes. If all the tiny, fresh water crustaceans disappeared, the hydras would go hungry. But all these "ifs" seldom happen. Under natural conditions, undisturbed by man, there is almost always just about the right number of each kind of living thing to balance the needs and services of all the rest.

Even in the jungle, where climatic conditions produce such luxuriant plant growth, there is never chaos. The delicate balance of nature is still preserved. Leaves, fruits and nuts of trees provide food for the wide variety of birds and mammals. Fallen and rotted vegetation provides a living for countless myriads of bacteria which convert it into nitrogen-rich manure. The jungle even has its own cleansing and sanitary system. When a bird or an animal dies, there are insects which quickly pick the carcass clean, or burying beetles ready to perform the function which gives them their name.

In the jungle, as elsewhere in nature, there are creatures which kill and creatures which are doomed to be killed, predators which eat and prey which is eaten. But the jungle is not a battlefield in the accepted sense. Killing and eating are matters of necessity, not of wanton cruelty. They are part of the natural mechanism for keeping the balance properly adjusted.

In a pond, every plant and every animal has something to offer, something to accept, from the other inhabitants. Even in the jungle nature holds a strict balance between the many different forms of life.

When Man Tilts Nature's Balance

When the balance of nature is disturbed, for whatever reason, the results may well be disastrous. It may happen, for instance, that prolonged gales drive the woodpeckers away from a pine forest. For years past they have kept down the numbers of bark-beetles which live just below the bark of the trees. When the birds disappear the bark-beetles multiply at a great rate and severely damage the new wood which the trees form each year. After a time the whole forest becomes tinder-dry, and a single stroke of lightning may set it ablaze.

All too often in the past man has tilted nature's balance with disastrous results: sometimes disastrous to other living things, sometimes disastrous to himself. While men remained wandering hunters and food-gatherers, they fitted into nature's pattern in much the same way as other creatures do. When, some ten thousand years ago, they first began to sow and reap crops, things changed. Now that they had a more reliable and more abundant food supply, their numbers began to increase more rapidly. With each passing century they needed more land for cultivation and pasturage.

We can see the result whenever we take a long journey through one of the thickly populated countries of Western Europe. For mile after mile we pass a pleasant but monotonous succession of meadows and tilled fields where once there were heaths, marshes, forests, prairies. In this modern landscape, where only a few species of grasses and flowers predominate, there is no longer a place for the many plants and animals which once made their homes in a wide variety of different habitats.

This has meant disaster and perhaps extinction to certain species. But in his quest for more agricultural land man has often brought near-disaster upon himself. In ancient times the Middle East and the lands bordering the Mediterranean Sea were the cradle of many great civilizations. Yet today, little remains of several of these civilizations, except a few ruined buildings surrounded by vast stretches of desert.

These deserts (middle picture) are largely man-made. Over many years, large numbers of sheep and goats gradually thinned out the grass and left the soil almost bare. Forests, which once broke the force of the wind and conserved the moisture in the soil, were recklessly cleared. Then winds, sweeping across the unsheltered and already partially bare land, slowly but relentlessly stripped it of its top-soil.

In more recent times, too, man has felled forests on hillsides. Heavy rains, which were once largely absorbed by the roots of the thirsty trees, now rush unchecked down the cleared slopes, carrying soil with them. The streams and rivers into which the mud-laden waters flow gradually become silted up and shallow. Unchecked winds also help to carry away soil. Little by little the region becomes a new desert.

In the industrial age, man has disturbed the balance of nature in a new way. Waste products from factories and chemical plants have been allowed to find their way into rivers and waterways. Where pollution has been severe many water plants have dried out. In time life becomes impossible for fishes and other forms of animal life. But a large variety of single-cell organisms (top right), principally bacteria, live and multiply in the tainted waters. Some are dangerous to human health and make bathing a highly hazardous pastime. Their presence sometimes causes considerable expense in purifying drinking water.

It is easy to condemn man's behavior in these matters, but few of us would wish to "go back to nature" to the extent of becoming hunters and foragers once more. More wisely, modern man is diligently seeking to learn more about how nature keeps her balance, so that if he tilts it in one direction he will know how to counterbalance it in another.

In ancient times man created deserts by overgrazing and tree-felling (center). Clearing hillside forests still causes erosion (bottom). Industrial waste poisons water but some unicellular organisms and microbes may live.

Butterflies as Long-Distance Travelers

From season to season conditions in many habitats change considerably. During winter, for instance, a temperate woodland cannot offer a good living to many of the birds which thrive there in summer. The migration of birds then helps nature to hold the balance of life.

Stories of bird migration have fascinated people for many generations, but it is only in comparatively recent times that men have discovered that certain butterflies, far smaller and frailer than any bird, also undertake long seasonal flights to distant lands. One species, the Canadian Monarch, spends the summer months near the western part of the border between Canada and the U.S.A. At the end of the summer it sets off either for Florida or Lower California, some 3,000 miles away, and spends the winter there. In spring it flies north again, lays its eggs, and soon afterwards dies.

Other great butterfly-travelers are the Atalantas (top left) which spend part of the summer in England and other areas of northwest Europe. We may see them as late as September or early October, feeding on plums that have fallen in orchards, but very soon afterwards they disappear. They have not died, but have migrated to Mediterranean lands.

Naturalists have studied the migrations of this species in some detail, and the four diagrams around the picture of the Atalanta sum up much of the information they have gathered. The Roman numeral at the center of each diagram is the number of the month it deals with (e.g. V and VI, in the top left-hand diagram, mean May and June). The total number of black butterfly-symbols in each diagram represents the proportion of the Atalanta population migrating during that period, and the letters N, S, E and W indicate in which direction they migrate.

In May and June rather less than a quarter migrate, flying mainly in a northerly direction. Almost as many take off during the single month of July, still flying mostly to the north. In August the total rises slightly and most of the migrants are now moving in a westerly, northerly or north-westerly direction. In September and October the migration reaches its peak, and by far the greater number of butterflies travel southward to warmer lands. The first Atalantas we see the following spring are not hatched out here. They are descendants of last season's travelers, and have themselves flown here from the south.

Perhaps the majority of far-faring butterflies travel by day, as do those shown in the top right-hand picture. The top one is the Thistle Vanessa, and its migrations were among the first to arouse curiosity, especially in England. Newspapers of the time carried such headlines as "Help Us to Solve the Great Butterfly Mystery". And, indeed, solving it was not an easy task. Many Vanessas had to be caught, given a distinctive mark and released. Then the help of large numbers of observant amateur naturalists had to be enlisted to report on their whereabouts later on.

Some migrating butterflies, including those shown in the bottom picture, are night-flyers. These nocturnal butterflies or moths all have one outstanding characteristic in common. They are all heavily built and have a stocky outline. One of the best-known species is the Death's Head Sphinx, whose soft rattling flight can sometimes be heard over potato fields.

There is still much research to be done into butterfly migrations, but already naturalists have learned a great deal. They know, for instance, that during migration butterflies obtain extra energy and warmth by drawing on reserves of fat accumulated in their bodies at an earlier stage. They have also recognized that there may be some connection between endurance in flight and coloring, for the brightest colored butterflies are commonly those which undertake the longest flights. But so far very little is known with certainty about how these small creatures find their way over vast distances.

TOP LEFT: The Atalanta, and diagrams to show when, where and in what numbers it migrates. RIGHT: Two butterfly migrants which fly by day. BOTTOM: Three, more heavily built, which travel by night.

Ocean Journeys
of Salmon and Eels

Many creatures besides birds and butterflies change their place of residence from time to time, and very often these movements take place at a particular stage in their life history.

The nymph of the dragonfly, for instance, develops from an egg laid in water; it climbs the stem of a water plant into the fresh air only just before it sheds its old skin and emerges as an adult dragonfly. Many shellfish spend the early part of their lives among the current-borne plankton near the surface of the sea, yet as adults they may hardly ever leave the sea floor. The land crabs of the West Indies and neighboring areas live as adults on hillsides half a mile or more from the shore, yet they lay their eggs in the sea, and their young live by the sea's edge until they are sufficiently developed to travel and find food inland.

Fishes, with few exceptions, are compelled to spend their whole lives in water, yet some of them make amazingly long seasonal journeys and amazing changes of habitat. Salmon spend late spring and summer in the open sea. In autumn, when they are plump and in the height of condition, they make their way towards river-mouths and begin swimming strongly upstream. When they reach rapids or small waterfalls they leap high out of the water and up into the next level. By late autumn they have reached quiet fresh water shallows far from the sea, sometimes even in mountain regions. There they lay their eggs and spend much of the winter. Then in early spring the adult salmon, now thinner and lacking the silver shine they had in autumn, set off downstream towards the open sea once more.

The young salmon which hatch from the eggs spend a long time in the upper reaches of the river, but when they reach the adult stage they too make straight for the sea.

From time to time naturalists have caught young salmon, marked them, and put them back into rivers. Salmon marked in this way have later been found many miles out to sea and sometimes near the shores of neighboring countries. When the time comes for the new generation of salmon to spawn, they commonly return to the same fresh water regions where they themselves were hatched.

The migration of eels is possibly even more astonishing. They spend several years of their early life in lakes and rivers, often taking refuge in mud during the winter months. By the end of that time the females may reach a length of four feet and weigh twelve pounds or more. The far smaller males may measure some eighteen inches long and weigh about a quarter of a pound.

Fully grown (7), the eels now set out on a journey of perhaps 2,000 miles to the Sargasso Sea, an area of the Atlantic Ocean abounding with plant life. There they lay their eggs at a considerable depth and, after a short time, die.

After some days, tiny transparent creatures only a quarter of an inch long (1) hatch from the eggs. Soon they come near the surface, and with an abundant food supply around them they grow steadily. By the end of the first summer they are an inch long. Then they begin to make their way northwards and later (if they are European eels) eastwards, aided by ocean currents. The whole ocean journey takes several years, and while making it the young eels not only grow to several inches in length, but also change from a flat to a long and rounded shape. Pictures 2 to 6 show stages in their development during the journey.

On reaching Europe, they make their way up rivers and into lakes where they live the rest of their lives until, as fully-grown eels, it is their turn to make the long return journey to the Sargasso Sea to breed.

TOP: Salmon leap upstream on the way to their breeding grounds. BOTTOM: Diagram (left) shows journey of young eels from Sargasso Sea to European rivers and return journey of adult eels. Map gives idea of distances involved.

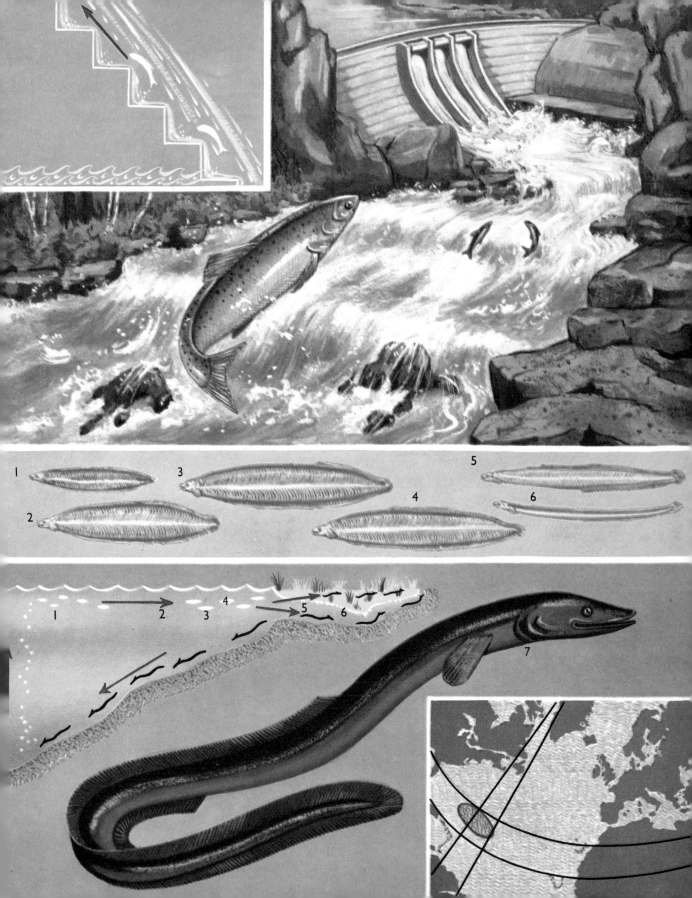

Knowns
and Unknowns
of Bird Migration

Naturalists know far more about the migrations of birds than about those of any other great section of the animal kingdom. Yet even the most experienced ornithologist would admit that many mysteries still remain.

The routes which birds follow have in many cases been studied very thoroughly. The ringing of thousands of birds in natural reserves and the collection of reports about their later whereabouts has proved a very effective method of research. It seems that many migrating birds, like modern airliners, keep to well-defined air corridors. Four of these great trunk routes are shown in different colors on the map opposite. Four birds, each of which flies along one of these routes, are shown on backgrounds of corresponding colors.

The Alaskan sedge warbler, on the red background, flies south-southwest across the Pacific to Hawaii. The Canadian sedge warbler (green background) flies over the coast of Labrador, southward across the western Atlantic, then over a great stretch of South America until it reaches the pampas of Argentina. Many European storks (yellow background) follow roughly the line of the Nile Valley, then continue southwards for hundreds of miles into South Africa; others, flying mainly from southwest Europe, cross the Sahara to West Africa. Some Siberian woodcocks (blue background) travel from eastern Siberia to Indo-China while others make their way to Australia.

Much is known, too, about the times of bird migrations. The grey crane (bottom left) begins leaving Western Europe in mid-September. The exodus reaches its climax in October, and all of the species have gone by early November.

The remaining six birds on the lower right are: (top) nightingale, hoopoe, swallow; (bottom) golden oriole, starling, and house martin. These birds, too, come and go as if to a timetable.

The nightingale flies away from its summer quarters in Western Europe, usually by night, between August and October, returning towards the middle of April. The hoopoe leaves Europe in September and October, returning towards mid-May. Swallows do not all leave in a single body. Among older birds, the date of departure depends largely on how many separate families they have reared during the season; among young birds it depends on when they were hatched. But most swallows leave by late September, while there are still many insects on the wing, and return in late March or early April. Swallows ringed in Western Europe have been reported in winter in French Guinea, Nigeria and the Belgian Congo.

The golden oriole migrates southward between July and late September, passes the winter in tropical East Africa and returns northward in April or early May. The house martin leaves Europe during late summer or early autumn, winters as far afield as India or South Africa, and returns at any time between mid-April and mid-June. Not all starlings migrate. In latitudes and climates like those of England, they may be permanent residents.

How do birds know when to migrate? Some scientists conclude that it is by the action of certain hormones, but they have not fully explained why these hormones are produced only at one particular time. Again, how do birds find their way over such vast distances? Young swallows and other young birds often undertake their first long flight unaccompanied by their elders. Nobody can yet tell us with certainty how they do it.

Samuel Butler pointed out that from the moment of birth we carry out our own process of metabolism—a far more complex business than playing a violin concerto—without ever being taught. He suggested we might do this because of some inherited "unconscious memory". Perhaps birds, too, possess some similar inheritance which makes their migrations possible.

Map showing flight-routes of the four birds on backgrounds of corresponding colors. BOTTOM: the grey crane and six other migratory birds of Europe: nightingale, hoopoe, swallow, golden oriole, starling, and house martin.

Uninvited Guests
and Unwilling Hosts

Plants and animals of one kind or another find a home almost everywhere on earth, from the peaks of high mountains to the deep troughs of oceans. Various living organisms are capable of finding food not only on the solid earth and in the air but also in deep waters where the sun's rays never penetrate. But perhaps one of the strangest modes of life is that followed by parasites—plants or animals which live, sometimes quite literally, "on the backs" of others.

The tremendous number and variety of parasites is as amazing as anything in nature. Scientists are still discovering hitherto unsuspected ones on all manner of creatures. There is an old rhyme which says that small fleas have smaller fleas upon their backs to bite 'em. It is not as far-fetched as it once seemed, for we now know that minute parasitic organisms frequently do live on or inside the bodies of other parasites. Many parasites live on the surface of their hosts and feed on their blood, others prey only on the food their hosts eat.

One blood-drinker most of us are familiar with is the mosquito. With its monotonous whine, it forms one of the few drawbacks to a warm summer evening. Whenever one drones around us we are usually ready to swat it, for we know that it is really and truly after our blood. In fact, without an occasional feed of human blood the female mosquito of the species shown in the top picture could never lay any eggs after the first batch. When it alights on its victim, it pushes its sharp, needle-like proboscis deep into the skin, injects a tiny amount of acid, and drinks its fill of blood.

The amount of blood it takes is very small and insignificant. The acid it injects may cause a certain amount of irritation but nothing worse. If the story ended there we could write the insect off as a mere nuisance. Yet in hot countries mosquitoes have been one of man's deadliest enemies

for many centuries. The reason lies in far smaller parasites *which live on them;* for feeding first on the blood of one man then on the blood of another, mosquitoes carry disease germs which, between times, have been parasites in their own small bodies.

In India, even in recent years, forty per cent of all deaths were due to malaria spread by this tiny insect. In Central America, mosquitoes carried the yellow fever germ which killed thousands of men working on the first Panama Canal project. Fortunately man is at last finding efficient ways of killing mosquitoes in large numbers while they are still water-borne larvae. But the battle still remains a grim one where swamps provide abundant breeding grounds.

Less deadly, but perhaps even more objectionable than mosquitoes, is the bedbug which depends entirely on man for food. This insect thrives best in old, dirty, over-crowded buildings where it can hide easily and find a plentiful food supply. By night it crawls from its hiding place, perhaps between floorboards; then, attracted by the smell of human breath, it finds its way to a sleeping victim. It punctures his skin, regurgitates the remains of its last meal into his veins, then takes a fresh meal. Before feeding, the hungry bug has a paper-thin body. After a feed its body is blown up like a balloon.

The bite of a bug can be a nuisance, and often leaves a swollen, itching mark on human skin. However, bugs seldom transmit diseases as deadly as malaria.

For the vast majority of us today bugs parasitic on man are more a curiosity of the past than a pest still to be feared. Modern standards of cleanliness have almost eliminated these insects in the western world, at least. But we often see their close relations, some of which live as parasites on other creatures. Our bottom picture shows a species of bug feeding from a living caterpillar.

Top pictures show, greatly enlarged, how a female mosquito and a bedbug feed on human blood. Bottom pictures show a relative of the bedbug about to feed on a caterpillar.

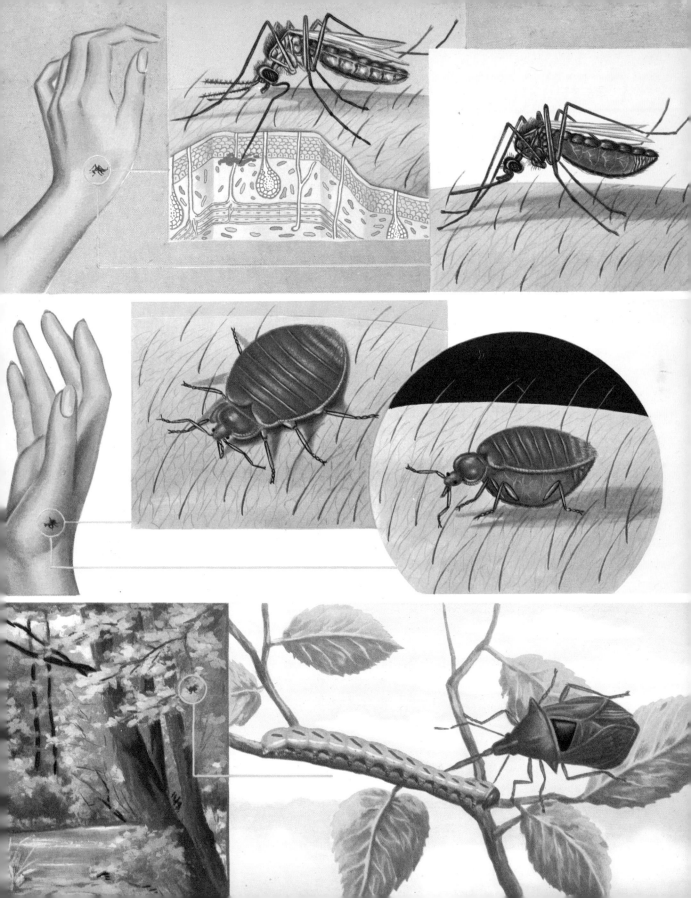

Eaten out of House and Home

Biologists and nature-lovers alike find the vast number of different ways in which parasites live a fascinating study. Here we can look at only a few of the most dramatic life stories.

Most of us think of parasites as creatures too small to be noticed in everyday life or perhaps as organisms which live in remote habitats. Yet the top picture on the facing page shows a feathered parasite which we all know. We may not all have seen and recognized the big, grey, hawk-like cuckoo, but we have all heard the male cuckoo's call.

Throughout the greater part of its life the cuckoo earns its own living like any other bird, but it simply will not hatch its own eggs or find food for its own young ones. Each May the female cuckoo lays her eggs in the nests of other, smaller birds, one egg to each nest she visits. In due course small hedge-sparrows, wagtails, pipits and robins become the cuckoo's unpaid baby-sitters. Soon after the baby cuckoo hatches out, it is far bigger than all the other babies in the nest. Often it grows bigger than its foster mother. It throws the other young birds from their own nest and greedily eats all the rations that the foster parents provide.

Cuckoos are parasites on other species of bird, but there is a deep-sea fish which becomes a parasite on another member of its own species. A pair of such fishes are pictured opposite. The female is easy enough to see, but the male, a mere fraction of her size, has fixed himself by suckers to his mate's head, where he protrudes like some strange horn. While the male fish is young and still a free-swimming creature, he has great difficulty in finding both food and a mate in the immensity of the dark waters. When he *is* fortunate enough to find a part-ner he attaches himself to her permanently. His life now literally depends on her. Not only does she provide his sole means of defense, but he actually draws nourishment for the rest of his life from her bloodstream.

If you look carefully on old walls or in woods near cabbage patches you may come across the shrivelled skins of dead caterpillars—those of the cabbage white butterfly. At first glance you might imagine that some of them were covered in yellow eggs. In fact they are not eggs but cocoons of ichneumon fly larvae. The female fly actually lays her eggs inside a young caterpillar. The eggs hatch and the larvae feed on their host. As they grow, the caterpillar weakens and at last dies. By this time the young parasites inside are ready to crawl out and begin turning into adult insects.

There are many kinds of ichneumon fly, all of which lay their eggs in living caterpillars. Some confine their egg-laying to one type of caterpillar, others are indiscriminating in their choice.

Occasionally a caterpillar victim is well grown when attacked. In that case it may even become a chrysalis in the normal way. But while the out-side case of the chrysalis appears normal, the transformation going on inside may produce not a hawk moth (bottom right) but its dreaded parasite, an ichneumon fly.

In the insect world there are several creatures which behave rather like the cuckoo. Indeed, one beetle is still more clever. It gets to its host's nest by using the host as a means of transport. This little parasite lives its adult life among flowers, but its young must feed on honey. Thus it must lay its eggs in a bumble bee's nest.

The beetle lurks in a flower until a bee arrives to gather nectar. As soon as it sees the bee's probos-cis appear, it seizes hold with its mandibles. The bee, taken by surprise, flees to the safety of its own nest. The little beetle could ask for nothing better!

The cuckoo which lays eggs in other birds' nests; a fish which clings to its mate's head; a fly which lays eggs in a caterpillar; a beetle which gets a ride to a bumble bee's nest; a fly which has hatched from the chrysalis of a moth.

Life on a Green Leaf

We have all noticed the little "apples" that grow on the underside of oak leaves. If you cut open one the size of that marked (A) in the top right-hand picture you may find a tiny maggot (1). Illustration (2) shows the same creature, somewhat magnified. It is really the larva of a gall wasp. Indeed "oak gall" is the correct name for what we commonly call an oak apple.

Inside the oak gall, the legless larva feeds on the walls of its vegetable prison. By late autumn it has reached full size and is ready to become an adult gall wasp (3).

Gall wasps are members of the hymenoptera, or membrane-winged insects (as opposed to beetles which are coleoptera, or sheath-wings). Though they are such tiny fragile insects, gall wasps in a sense build their own cradle-prisons, many times their own size.

A female gall wasp inserts her ovipositor, or egg-laying tube, into a young oak leaf and lays an egg. As she does so, she injects the leaf with a substance which stimulates growth in the plant cells. The cells go on multiplying until they produce a swelling that encases the egg. When it hatches, the larva feeds on these cells and also injects them with a liquid which encourages them to continue growing. The oak gall then forms around its strange prisoner.

The oak tree itself manufactures the vegetable cells that make the gall wasp's home. Thus it almost seems that the tree encourages these parasites to prey on it. Yet the benefits are one-sided. Though several oak galls may grow on one leaf, seemingly without interfering with its normal growth, they certainly do nothing to assist that growth.

The gall wasp which gives rise to oak apples is but one of many kinds of insect which can change plant growth to suit their own purposes. Certain other species of wasp and mosquito also produce gall nuts. People who specialize in the subject tell us that different species of insects inject various plants with different substances. All these substances give rise to harmless "vegetable tumors", and each kind of insect produces a different kind of tumor.

In contrast to the round house of the gall wasp, another insect lives in an irregular shaped home which forms on an oak twig. The illustration (B), black center panel, shows this gall, first actual size, then magnified several times.

To nature-lovers, oak galls are curiosities. To farmers, galls on fruit trees can be pests. Some galls cause pears to drop from the trees before they are fully formed.

Those of us who are fond of gardens or gardening are more familiar with another form of life on a leaf—the greenfly. Unlike gall wasps which use a plant as a cradle, greenflies make life-long use of roses as a canteen. Our illustration shows a typical greenfly colony swarming on a rose stem. Magnified are a winged male and two different kinds of wingless females.

When they are fully fed, greenflies secrete a liquid very much coveted by ants. The greenfly itself becomes the creature preyed upon when ants carry it to their nest and make use of its sweet liquid as men make use of cow's milk.

Ants also prey upon the larva of the froghopper, a small insect rather like a short-legged grasshopper. Few of these soft-skinned larvae would survive both the attack of ants and the glare of the sun without the protection of the home they build around themselves. These larvae cover themselves with a mass of frothy bubbles. The illustration (bottom right) shows the bubbles, often called cuckoo-spit (1), as well as a larva (2) and the adult froghopper (3).

The larva bites into the soft stem of a plant and sucks out sap which passes through its body, mixing with a waxy secretion. Then it withdraws its beak-like mouth from the stem and breathes in. Some of the air passes through its body and blows the sap-and-wax mixture into a mass of concealing and protecting foam.

LEFT: Greenflies on a rose bush. RIGHT: (above) Oak galls and gall wasp; (below) a froghopper uses plants to help it make a protective covering of bubbles.

♂

♀ ♀

A

2 3 1

B

2 3 1

Plants which Live on Plants

We have already noticed many animals which live on plants, animals which live on other animals, and even a few plants which feed on insects. But there are also plants which live as parasites on other plants. They find homes ranging from the dark depths of the soil to the topmost twigs of substantial trees.

Mistletoe, which most of us associate with Christmas and perhaps seldom see outside a shop, is such a tree-top parasite. On a winter's day, when oaks, elms, pears and poplars are stripped of leaves, you may sometimes catch sight of green clusters crowning their bare branches. Indeed it may have been this unseasonable splash of color that made primitive peoples think of mistletoe as a plant apart—a sacred bough. Writings some two thousand years old record that in certain European lands, priests once guarded with their lives the groves where this sacred plant flourished, and only cut it on ceremonial occasions, using a sickle of precious metal.

They were in fact tending what foresters would class as a pest, for mistletoe lives at the expense of the tree it grows on. Unlike ivy, which is rooted in the ground, mistletoe thrusts its roots into the bark and a woody part of a branch and taps its nourishing sap.

How does mistletoe reach these branches in the first place? It depends very largely on the appetite which many birds have for its succulent white berries. A thrush which has had a meal of mistletoe berries may fly to another tree and clean its beak on a branch. There it may leave a tiny mistletoe seed embedded in a crack in the bark. Soon the seed splits open to release a sliver of root which multiplies into several rootlets, all twisting and probing for holds. Once the plant is established, its own leaves can take carbon dioxide gas from the atmosphere, but its roots must absorb mineral salts and water from the host tree.

Our top pictures show that in summer the host tree (here an oak) seems to be perfectly normal; only in winter do its bare branches reveal the presence of the parasite mistletoe.

While one parasite plant is sprouting from its upper branches, a tree may be supporting other parasites in or near its roots. These are often fungi —a large group of plants which includes mushrooms, toadstools, molds and rusts. Such plants contain no chlorophyll and are therefore unable to manufacture their own food. The center pictures show a fungus sometimes called the honey mushroom, which thrives on many kinds of tree, living or dead. The name comes not from its taste, which is far from honey-like, but from the yellow-brown color of its caps. These caps carry the tiny spores which can grow into full-size fungi themselves. Some parts of the fungus shown in our picture have the property of being faintly luminous at night. It is possible that they gave rise to many of the old country tales of will o' the wisps and hobgoblins seen in dark woods.

Though evils of that kind are fictitious, the damage which this strange fungus does is very real. With its long, branching vegetable parts (which serve as a kind of root) going deep into growing trees, it can transform valuable timber into a worthless waste of rotting branches.

The most spectacular fungus of all is the Rafflesia arnoldi (bottom), which grows in the forests of Sumatra and which produces the largest flower on earth. This jungle fungus grows on the woody roots of climbing plants, and its huge flowers look as if they are part of the host plant. As mere buds, these flowers may be as big as a fair-sized cabbage. It may take as much as a month before they open and reach full size—about a yard across, and with petals half an inch thick. Then in a few days they fade and wither. But meanwhile their unpleasant smell has attracted enough insects to ensure fertilization.

ABOVE: Oak tree and close-up of parasitic mistletoe. MIDDLE: Two dwelling places (left) of a fungus (right) which can cause serious damage to growing trees. BOTTOM: The giant flowers of a jungle parasite.

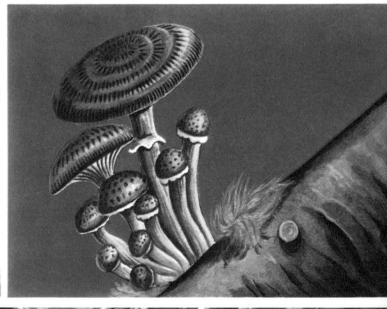

Worms which Live in Human Beings

Man himself is the host for a number of parasites, some of which prey on him internally and some of which prey on the surface of his body. Among the internal parasites are the notorious tapeworms and threadworms.

For long, tapeworms posed man a problem. Where did they come from? How did they get inside the human body? How could man rid himself of such a horrible pest?

Tapeworms may attain a truly incredible length. Our illustrations show the length of three different kinds, by means of black lines drawn to the same scale as the three men. Each tapeworm is made up of many segments. You can see them, magnified, opposite. At one end is the tiny scolex, or head, equipped with hooks and suckers which enable it to cling to the wall of the human intestine.

The tapeworm itself has no intestine and no mouth by which it can take in nourishment. Instead of feeding as we do, it absorbs food through its skin. It needs, and has, no digestive system as complicated as our own, for the food it absorbs is already digested by its human host.

So well adapted is the creature to its parasitic way of life that it has dispensed with almost every organ not essential to its existence. Yet its reproductive organs are exceptionally well developed.

Each segment of its body is virtually a self-sufficient tapeworm, largely filled with reproductive cells. From time to time a segment breaks off from the worm and finds its way to the outside world. Occasionally a pig may eat one of these segments. The eggs then hatch out in its stomach as tiny embryos which bore into the pig's blood vessels and thus find their way into its muscles.

For centuries people knew of these "bladder-worms" (shown in blue) but no one connected them with the immensely long worms known to infest man. No one realized that if man swallowed pork in which these tiny worms still lived they would develop into tapeworms inside his own body.

Now that we do have this knowledge, we are using it to ensure that modern man shall no longer suffer from this scourge of his ancestors. Before meat appears in our stores, government inspectors examine it to make sure that it is free from parasitic worms. Pork infected with "bladder-worm" looks measly. Since this parasite cannot live long in very high temperatures, we can further safeguard ourselves by seeing that all the meat we eat is thoroughly cooked.

So far we have looked only at the tapeworm which spends part of its life inside the pig—the worm which is also most common in man. As our pictures show, there are other tapeworms living a double life. In fact, of the three pictured, the one from pork is the smallest—about twice the length of a man. Another, living part of its time in the cow, is six times the length of a man, while one which is parasitic on the freshwater pike is seven times a man's length. Though they live in similar environments, each of these different tapeworms has adapted itself in slightly differing ways, as you can see by comparing the shape of their segments, or proglottides, and the shape of their heads (magnified within white circles).

To people in hot, eastern countries several internal parasites still remain a serious threat to health. A common scourge is the worm-like trichina. Our illustration (bottom left) shows the larvae of four trichinae inside the muscle of a pig, its host. The law of Moses forbidding people to eat pork was a wise precaution during the long trek from Egypt to Canaan, when ill-cooked pork could have caused many deaths among the Israelites.

To people in the western world only the parasitic worm pictured at the bottom right remains a frequent pest. This threadworm (greatly magnified) afflicts children with its irritating movements; but fortunately it is not equipped with strong hooks or suckers and is easily eliminated from the body.

ABOVE: Three kinds of tapeworm. BOTTOM LEFT: Trichinae in muscle of pork. BOTTOM RIGHT: Threadworm.

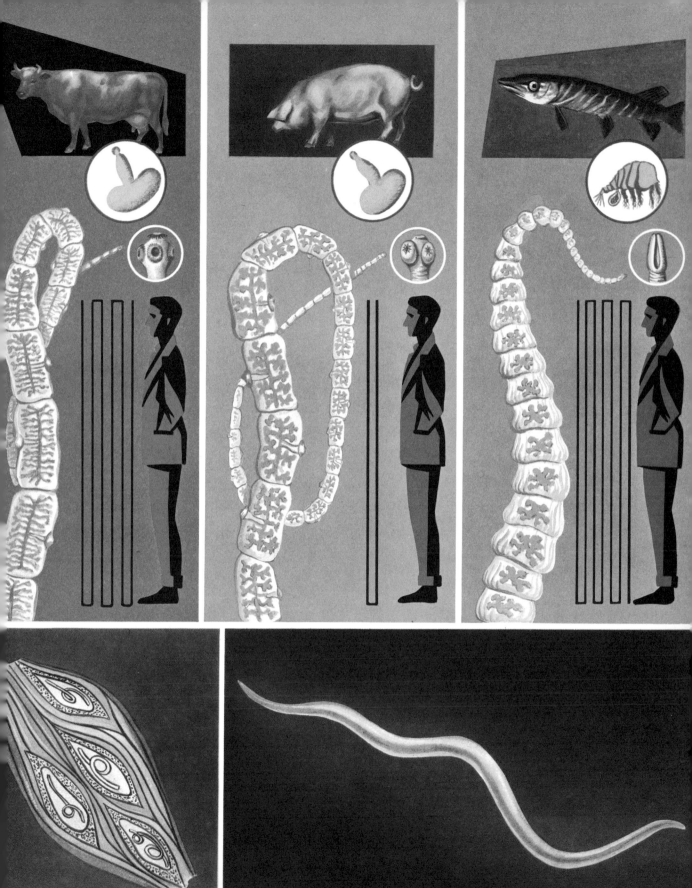

"Vampires" that Leap, Burrow or Cling

In addition to internal parasites, man is also subject to the attentions of several creatures which make a permanent or temporary home on his skin. Miniature "vampires" which feed on human blood include fleas.

Different varieties of flea thrive throughout the world. In Europe alone there are over 150 kinds. Fortunately not all of them live on man. Many mammals and birds possess their own special fleas and flea-like parasites. The fleas which attach themselves to dogs are quite different from those which attach themselves to man, though people may occasionally pick up the former as accidental passengers.

The top picture shows the sort that lives on man, greatly enlarged. In fact, a flea is only about a twelfth of an inch long, and it would take many thousands of them to weigh an ounce. Yet, as an attraction in side-shows at fairs, people have contrived minute carriages and persuaded fleas to pull them with a harness of gold thread. The picture which shows this gives a more accurate idea of the size of a flea.

These tiny wingless insects can make enormous leaps, sometimes to a height several hundred times that of their own bodies. By contrast, man at first seems a clumsy, earthbound creature, for even the world's record high jumper cannot leap much more than the height of his own head.

One might be tempted to think that if a man had the same strength, in proportion to his size, as a flea has, he could leap over the highest skyscraper. But that kind of reasoning is far from sound. As the size of creatures increases, their weight goes up out of all proportion to their increase in muscular strength. In fact if a flea *were*

as big as a man its weight would be such that its increased strength would not be enough to lift it very far. You might enter it in a hurdle race against a man and find that the man was a good match for it.

Like bugs, fleas feed on human blood. Also like bugs, they spend only part of their time on the human body. They lay their eggs in some dusty corner or between floorboards. The eggs hatch into worm-like larvae which feed on various kinds of refuse. Then, after metamorphosis, they become adult fleas.

In the tropics, a particularly unpleasant type of flea makes its home not on, but *in* man's skin. The adult female buries itself in human skin, often beneath a toenail, leaving only a tiny part of its body protruding. As our bottom pictures show, this insect is quite small, but once it is "dug in" and has begun to suck blood, it swells up into an unrecognizable balloon the size of a garden pea. No wonder it causes its victim intense pain.

The creature shown at the bottom right of the facing page is unlike the common flea or the bedbug in that it spends its entire life on man. This parasite is the head-louse, and its chosen home is among the hairs of unwashed human heads. It does not leap or fly. It has no need, for it never voluntarily leaves its host, and its strong grip ensures that its host cannot get rid of it merely by shaking his head.

The head-louse lays its eggs actually on the hairs of the head. Our enlarged picture shows them looking like some strange fungoid growths on each hair. The parent louse firmly glues its eggs in position with a sticky substance. When they hatch, they do not have to pass through a larval stage, in which they might be easily destroyed. Instead, they hatch into insects recognizably like their parents, and already equipped to feed on human blood.

Once a common flea has laid its eggs it probably never sees its offspring. Yet a head-louse may live on the same human head with several generations of its own descendants.

ABOVE: Flea magnified and performing fleas on human hand; man and flea as high jumpers. BELOW: A flea which burrows and swells in the skin; head-louse and its eggs on human hair, enlarged.

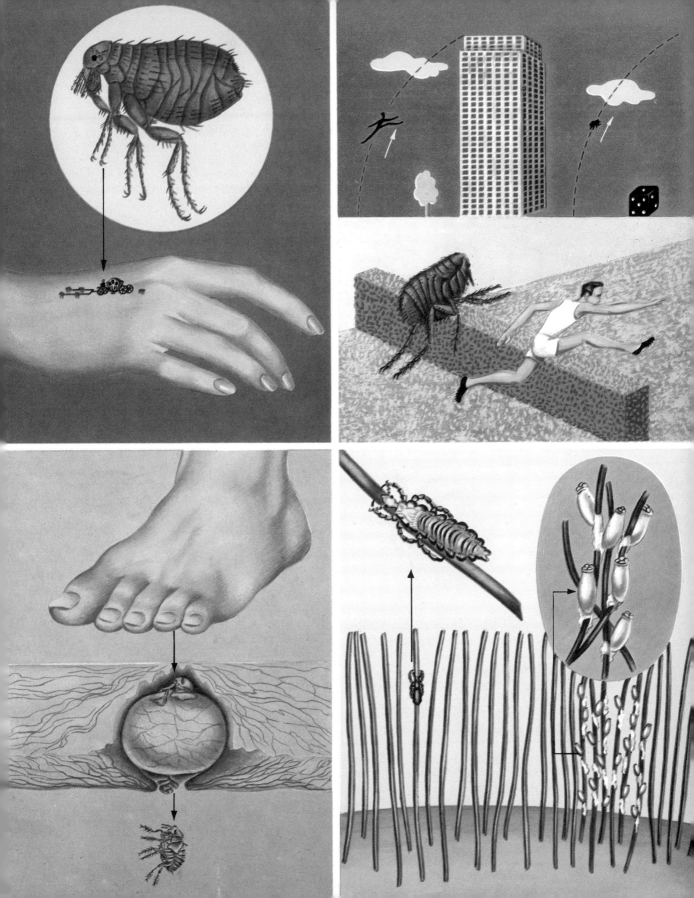

Living Together in Partnership

Even a quick look at the life-stories of a few parasites serves as a reminder that nature's world is not one of universal peace and friendship. Each species must put up a struggle for its existence: a struggle for living space, a struggle for food, a struggle against the attacks of its predators or against the defenses of its prey.

Yet nature can also show some remarkable examples of creatures of different kinds which live together in true partnership, each helping the other, each benefiting from the other's presence. Biologists call this kind of partnership symbiosis, which simply means "together-living". Like parasitism, symbiosis may be for a short period or for a lifetime; it may exist between two plants, two animals, or an animal and a plant.

An outstanding example of symbiosis between two plants is that which occurs when a fungus and an alga unite to form what we call lichen. The illustration (top left) shows lichen as we see it growing on a piece of bark or a stone wall. The greatly magnified view shows a cross section through it. You can clearly see the white tube-like filaments of the fungus and the thick layer of yellow cells which make up its outer surface. Just below these yellow cells, which contain no chlorophyll, is a layer of green cells. These cells, rich in chlorophyll, are the cells of the alga.

The fine tube-like filaments of the fungus draw up rainwater and provide the rootless alga with moisture. The green alga manufactures food from gases in the air and from the water which the fungus brings it. The fungus depends for its food on what the alga makes. Besides giving the alga water, the fungus also offers it security, for it produces an acid which eats into bare rock and provides rootholds. Lichen, which is thus really two plants living together almost like one, is frequently the first form of life to grow on scarcely-formed soil. As it dies it enriches the soil, and other plants can later flourish there.

Fungi can also live in symbiosis with the higher plants. If you dig up the roots of certain conifers, you may notice what looks like white felt clinging to their tips. This "felt" is really made up of filaments of a tiny fungus. Far from being a harmful parasite on the conifer, this fungus carries out work normally done by a tree's fine hair-like roots. It collects water and mineral salts which the tree can make use of. In exchange, it draws food from the tree—food which has been manufactured by green needles growing high above ground in the sunlight.

Hermit crabs provide an interesting study in symbiosis between animals. The hermit crab hides the soft hind part of its body in an empty mollusk shell. Sea-anemones often make their homes on the outside of the shell. This benefits the hermit crab, for these jelly-like animals which look like strange flowers can sting or discharge unpleasant fluids. Their presence serves to frighten off many of the larger sea-dwellers which might otherwise eat the crab. In turn, the sea-anemones gain by feeding on left-over scraps from the hermit crab's meals.

The top right-hand pictures (much enlarged) show stages in the life of a beetle which lives in symbiosis with a yeast. The yeast cells live inside the adult beetle (4). When the female lays her eggs (1) some of these cells adhere to the outside and multiply there. When the larva hatches out, it feeds on the vitamin-rich yeast and grows fast (3). Larvae deprived of this yeast do not reach full size (2), and may shrivel and die. When the healthy larvae turn into adult beetles they, of course, already have yeast cells living inside them, and the cycle is complete.

The yeast cells, too, benefit from this living together. They find better shelter and growing ground in the beetle than they would be likely to find elsewhere.

TOP LEFT: A lichen—two plants in one. TOP RIGHT: A beetle which houses the yeast which feeds its young. BOTTOM LEFT: A fungus and a tree which live as partners. BOTTOM RIGHT: Partnership of hermit crab and sea-anemones.

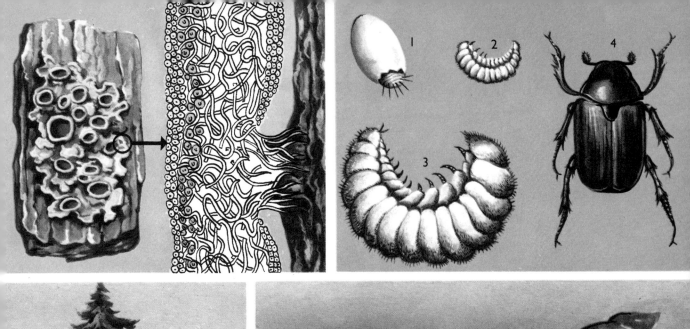

Strange Companions of the Waters

Seas and rivers provide many examples of creatures which live together as partners, though we are not always certain what benefits each partner derives from the arrangement.

The top left-hand picture shows several striped fish, some twenty to thirty inches long, swimming beside a shark. These fish stay close by their giant companion and follow every movement of its body. Often they swim just ahead of the shark. This habit gave rise to the belief that they were showing the shark which way to go, and earned them their popular name of pilot fish. But there is no evidence to prove that they really are pathfinders.

What is certain is the tenacity with which some pilot fish follow their chosen traveling companion. People who catch sharks have noticed that pilot fish sometimes circle their ship long after a shark is caught, as if awaiting its return. However, these fish doubtless change their allegiance from time to time. Sometimes they even adopt a ship and swim beside it for many miles, right into port. Probably some of them remain faithful to one shark for months while others frequently find new companions.

It may well be that the pilot fish find safety from other large fishes while they are near the shark, and they can certainly snap up any scraps left over from its huge meals. Yet no one knows precisely what benefits the shark gains. We only know that it certainly tolerates their presence.

Tropical seas, especially near coral reefs, are the home of countless soft-bodied animals and animal-colonies equipped with paralyzing stings and powerful tentacles. Many of these live fixed in one spot and depend for food on whatever the sea-currents bring within their reach. Nevertheless, like the Portuguese Man o' War shown on page 19, some of the larger ones are capable of killing and digesting any fish unwary enough to go near them.

Yet certain small fishes swim in and out among these killing stings and tentacles quite unharmed. Indeed, they seek refuge there when they are pursued by large and hungry fish. Some even lay their eggs there and the tentacles, as if somehow stimulated, spread out and protect them until the young ones hatch out.

In this extraordinary partnership the small fish gain refuge and protection. The animal-colonies also benefit, because the fish drop particles of food within the reach of their protectors, which would otherwise have to depend on plankton.

In the hieroglyphic script of ancient Egypt, in which every picture stood for an idea, a rough-and-ready drawing of a small long-legged bird occurs over and over again. Today this bird still thrives along the River Nile. The flash of its white plumage is a familiar sight as it suddenly takes to its wings and skims low over the water. We call it the crocodile bird. The Arabs call it the crocodile's lookout. Both names are apt.

These birds haunt swamps and sand banks frequented by crocodiles. Most creatures go in fear of their lives from these giant reptiles. But the crocodile birds grow up fearlessly among them. They will run along a giant crocodile's back as nonchalantly as a sparrow hops along a garden path.

They find insect parasites which bore into the reptile's tough hide and irritate it. Like living toothbrushes, they will even hop into the crocodile's gaping jaws to clear up scraps of food from between its sharp teeth. If danger approaches while the lazy crocodile basks asleep in the hot sunshine, the birds utter sharp cries which wake it instantly.

It is true that the crocodile and the crocodile birds seem to show nothing resembling affection for each other; theirs is purely a business partnership. But it is no less effective for that.

TOP LEFT: Striped pilot fish with a shark. TOP RIGHT: Some of the fish of tropical seas find protection among the stinging tentacles of various animal-colonies. BELOW: Crocodiles and the crocodile birds which keep their skins and teeth clean.

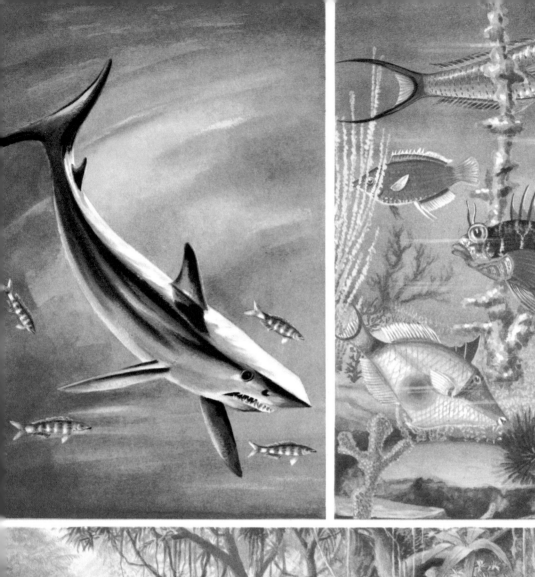

Partnerships between Flowers and Insects

Symbiosis does not always involve a permanent, or even a long-continued, association between the partners. It often happens that two quite different living things derive great help from each other as the result of no more than a fleeting contact. Pollination provides many examples of such short-lived but important partnerships.

Flowering plants which grow from seed can ensure the continued life of the species only if pollen from the stamen of the flower is carried to the stigma, from which it can travel down to the ovules, or unfertilized seeds, and fertilize them. In most cases there is a process of cross-fertilization. That is, pollen from the stamen of one flower is carried to the stigma of another flower of the same species, perhaps on the self-same plant, perhaps on a plant some distance away. In many species the pollen is simply carried from flower to flower by the wind. Such flowers, usually small, commonly have no scent and no nectar.

But a very large number of flowering plants depend on various members of the animal kingdom to carry their pollen. In return the plants provide these creatures with nectar which serves as food. In temperate lands flowers enter into such partnerships almost solely with insects, but in tropical countries humming birds and bats also serve as pollen-carriers. Indeed, in tropical South America a species of honeysuckle is visited by very small humming birds during the day and by some large moths by night. Both take nectar from the flower while hovering near it in mid-air, and at a distance the moth's long extended proboscis looks very much like the humming bird's needle-thin bill. The moth in question has been given the name of the humming bird hawk moth.

Some insects seem to be attracted by the scent of a particular flower, others by the color, still others by the size and shape. If every kind of insect visited every kind of flower, much pollen would be wasted by being dusted off on to the wrong flower species. But because different insects have these marked preferences for different scents and colors, much waste is avoided.

In Southern England there is a species of wasp which lives underground in winter. The males come out, in spring, before the females. They are strongly attracted to a flower of the orchid family which is then in bloom because they seem to mistake it for the female wasp.

As a different means of attracting the right insect guests, some plants, like that in the top left-hand picture, carry not only green leaves (A1) but also, near the tops of their stems, leaves of some other shade (A2), which throw the color of the flower (B) into sharp relief.

Some plants even seem to display signposts, pointing the way to their nectar. The flower of the forget-me-not family, shown in the top right-hand picture, stores its nectar deep inside its center. The entrance to the nectar-store is clearly marked by a bright yellow circle. Some naturalists call markings of this kind "honey signs".

Plants and animals sometimes enter into partnerships which serve a purpose other than pollination. In autumn many trees and shrubs, like that in the bottom picture, bear clusters of brightly colored berries. These berries, the fruit of the plant, contain seeds which are already fertilized. The berries provide many a bird with a good meal, but a bird's digestive system cannot assimilate the pips, or seeds.

The bird flies off, and in time the pips are expelled from its body with its droppings. There is a good chance that they will fall on open ground where they have room to take root and grow. If they had been left to fall from the boughs where they hung, they would have had little chance of growing, because there the spreading roots of the mother plant take too much moisture and nourishment from the soil.

TOP LEFT: Leaves of distinctive shade draw insects' attention to the flower. TOP RIGHT: Yellow circle points way to nectar-store. BOTTOM: A shrub provides a bird with food; the bird will carry seed to new ground.

Visitors Welcome and Unwelcome

For many a plant the question of whether or not it can attract the right insects is the same as the question of whether or not it can survive. If it cannot attract insects which will carry pollen from flower to flower and so fertilize its seeds, it will soon die out. It is therefore not surprising that in certain flowers there are strange and sometimes quite elaborate methods of making some insect visitors welcome and others unwelcome.

We are apt to associate flowers and winged insects with daylight and warm sunshine. But some flowers, such as night-scented stock, are more attractive by night than by day, because it is during the hours of darkness that their scent is strongest. Some winged insects, too, are nocturnal creatures, seeking food at night and resting by day. Various flowers depend on night-flying insects to carry their pollen, and have the means of attracting them in the dark.

The small white convolvulus shown in the top left-hand picture is a good example. Its nectar is stored deep down inside its long trumpet-shaped flower. Only a fairly big insect with a long proboscis can at once extract the nectar and get itself dusted with pollen from the stamens. One such insect is the night-flying hawk moth. The small white convolvulus makes the hawk moth welcome in three ways. First, unlike certain other kinds of convolvulus, it keeps its petals open at night. Next, it gives off its strongest scent by night. Finally, its white flower shows up clearly in all but the blackest nights, and serves as a lamp to light the hawk moth's way.

Some flowers might almost be said to keep their nectar locked away. Often in such cases, the only insects which hold the "key" are those which can help in pollination. One such flower, a native of Brazil, has a long, narrow, winding opening leading down into the nectar. Certain species of bee, perched just inside the flower where pollen rubs off on to their backs, can manage to extract it. Sometimes a moth which feeds while hovering on the wing attempts to do so. But its method of feeding would not help the flower. The moth can dip its long proboscis into the nectar, but, while hovering, can never pull it out again. It may well pay for its attempted robbery by being held prisoner until it starves to death.

The dead nettle (middle row of pictures) which is sometimes mistaken for a stinging nettle, also effectively locks out unwelcome visitors. A bumble bee with wings partially closed, can squeeze between the "lips" of the flowers, rubbing off pollen as it goes, and insert its proboscis into the nectar. Certain butterflies, though they may have an equally long proboscis, cannot do so. Their more rigid wings prevent them from passing between the flower's "lips".

The welcome insect-visitors are those which will pay for their meal by doing the job of pollen-carrying which the flower requires of them (bottom right). But flowers do not always succeed in getting the price they require.

Certain kinds of wild bee are equipped with only a short proboscis. They cannot possibly insert it deep into a trumpet-shaped flower and take the nectar in the orthodox way. They attack the flower from the outside, making their way down to the calyx, a kind of sheath round its base. There they make an incision and extract the nectar through it.

These unwelcome visitors certainly have no key to the nectar-store, but they can nevertheless ransack its contents. Like a safe-breaker, they take what they want without paying the proper price. In effect, they practice a special form of parasitism on the flowers they visit.

TOP: A flower shows a light for a welcome night visitor. CENTER: The bumble bee's wings and proboscis are its key to the dead nettle's nectar. BOTTOM: A wild bee prepares to break into a nectar-store, avoiding the job of carrying pollen which the flower requires as its price for a meal.

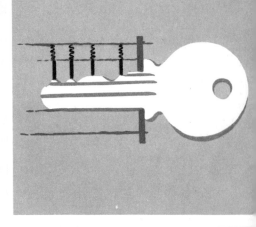

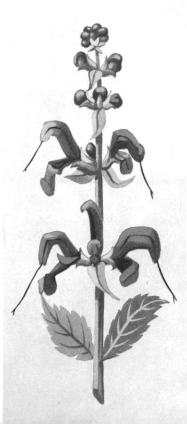

Using Disguise for Protection

Animals no less than plants must be able to ensure the survival of the species, for it seems evident that nature is far more concerned with the species than with the individual. No species— not even man—is so swift, so strong or so clever that every individual can be certain of escaping death from its enemies. But every species has some means by which enough of its members *can* escape to ensure that the species as a whole will survive. Those which are not endowed with great strength, speed or cunning are often able to escape the attentions of their enemies by means of disguise or camouflage.

Many animals of prey which must find their food among the wide-awake smaller animals of the jungle have spotted coats which make them hard to see against their dappled surroundings. The sea-horses of Australian waters, which could so easily be eaten by other sea creatures, have fins which are almost indistinguishable from the weeds where they hide. Long, slim pipe fishes living among long, slender eelgrass, are almost invisible.

Many insects are particularly successful wearers of disguise. The stick insect, which is a tropical relation of certain European grasshoppers, remains motionless during the day with its head drawn in between its legs. There is nothing to indicate to insect-eating birds that this little dried-up "twig" could move at all (top left). Yet when night falls and most birds go to roost, the little "twig" comes to life and sets out in search of its vegetable food.

Another expert in camouflage is the insect (top right) which lives in Central Asia. Its wings have the shape and color of a leaf. It is practically impossible to spot it when it is hidden among the green leaves of a plant. It almost seems that man is incapable of inventing anything which nature has not invented long ago, for this Asian insect and the stick insect were using camouflage long before soldiers learned to wear camouflage suits for jungle warfare.

Even more remarkable than the creatures which wear a permanent form of camouflage are those which can change their appearance to blend with whatever kind of background they happen to be near at any particular time. Certain animals can not only change their shade but even their actual color to match or blend with their immediate surroundings.

The center illustrations show how certain fish, dark in color, become brighter immediately upon leaving the gloomy deep waters and swimming up towards the sunlit surface.

The chameleon's ability to blend with its background (bottom) has become proverbial. It changes not only its shade of color but also the color itself, according to where it happens to be. Thus against a brown background it will be brown, against a green background, green. This change of color is brought about by an accumulation of pigment in the skin. The mechanism on which the phenomenon depends is regulated by the nervous system and by the operation of hormones. It appears that the eyes set the whole process in motion. According to what color they register, they transmit a signal to the nervous system which sets the hormones to work and also the pigmented cells. How the many pigments of different color cooperate as they do to produce the required change is one of the most remarkable things in the whole story of animal disguise.

Yet no disguise, however wonderful or efficient, gives an animal complete protection against all its enemies. A green caterpillar feeding on green leaves, for instance, is well protected from most insect-eating birds but its color is no protection at all against the ichneumon fly, which seeks out caterpillars not by their appearance but by their scent. Similarly, those fishes which change shade according to the degree of light in the water are not, because of that fact, safe from the baited hook of the fisherman, or the net of a trawler.

TOP: Insects more adept at camouflage than any modern troops. CENTER: A fish which becomes lighter as it moves into sunnier waters. BOTTOM: A chameleon, nature's great master of disguise.

Color for Hiding, Warning and Mimicry

Though there are few creatures which can change color as quickly and effectively as the chameleon, there are many which employ color even more subtly as a means of defense. It is possible for an animal to be the same color as its surroundings and yet to be clearly visible because of its tell-tale shadow. The green caterpillar in the circle (top left) avoids much of this danger. The underside of its body is a paler green than its back. All the while the light is above and behind it, the edge of its shadow falls on the pale green underside and the outline is so blurred that it can scarcely be noticed.

The butterfly shown below the caterpillar has orange-tipped wings and is easy to see while flying. But follow the white arrow and notice what happens when it alights. As it raises its wings to a resting position the inside surfaces, which are colored quite differently, scarcely show against the green foliage.

The moth (top right) has somewhat drab blue-grey front wings but brilliantly-colored back wings. Like the butterfly, it is easy to spot while flying, but when it settles it spreads its front wings backwards, covering the back ones completely. Its enemies would then be very unlikely to distinguish it from the bark of the tree where it rests.

Not all animals use color as camouflage. Some actually seem to use it to advertise their presence. Many creatures which are capable of inflicting poisoned stings or bites, for instance, are so colored as to be clearly visible from quite a distance away. In such cases the colors which serve as nature's warning notices are often black and yellow, sometimes black, yellow and red. All three colors are to be found on the poisonous South American snake shown center left.

Other animals which live in regions where these warning colors are common learn to shun them like the plague. Yet certain harmless and almost defenseless lizard-like creatures carry the same dreaded colors. Their sham warning-signals frighten off enemies with which they would otherwise be quite incapable of dealing.

The wasp (bottom left) carries clearly marked black and yellow warning rings. It is to its own advantage that other living things which fear its painful sting should remember the dreaded colors and keep away from it. But there is also a butterfly which carries the same colors as the wasp. Would-be enemies mistake the inoffensive butterfly for the dangerous wasp and keep clear of it. This butterfly does not use color for camouflage, but as a means of mimicking an insect more to be feared than itself.

Some insects are shunned by birds because they have an unpleasant taste or smell. Where such insects abound it is quite common to find others which are *not* distasteful but which bear very similar markings. Because of their similar colors, the latter are just as safe from birds as the former.

It is easy to understand how insects and other animals benefit by using color as a means of hiding or as a means of mimicking creatures more dangerous than themselves. It is not so easy to understand how genuinely dangerous animals such as poisonous snakes benefit by wearing bright colors as warning signals. Yet they undoubtedly do.

A snake has no particular interest in biting any creature which it does not intend to eat. Every time it inflicts a bite it is left comparatively weak and defenseless until its glands produce enough poison to replace what it has lost. Its poisonous fangs are weapons which it should use only as a last resort. By flaunting its colored danger signals it is able to conserve its venom almost entirely for the purpose of killing its prey. Venomous snakes which do not carry warning signals commonly have some other way of frightening enemies away, such as hissing, making a rattling sound, or rearing themselves up into threatening positions.

TOP: Insects bearing protective color camouflage. BELOW: (Left) Two creatures whose colors warn that they are dangerous. (Right) Two creatures which use colors to pretend they are dangerous.

Finding Safety in Numbers

Not all animals rely on color for protection. Many find a degree of safety and achieve a better livelihood by living together in groups of varying size.

The smallest and simplest community is the family, the members of which form a single close-knit unit. There are many examples of family life among birds, to which the nesting season is indispensable to the survival of the species. Often the family remains together until, and even after, the young ones are old enough to fend for themselves.

Among certain of the higher mammals the mother watches over and feeds the young for months; the father sometimes protects them for years. This is particularly so with a species of gibbon found in Siam. The family group consists of parents and young ones only. The mother gives birth to a young gibbon every two or three years and each young one remains with the family circle for up to twelve years. The family unit searches for food together, rests in the same spot together, and at certain hours of the day makes the jungle echo with their cries.

Several families of baboons (top left) unite to form a single small herd under the command of an old male baboon. The conduct of the herd seems to be regulated by strict laws and customs, and it is not unusual for the leader to act as a positive dictator, claiming all the females as his own wives. Other males have to use all the cunning they possess in order to find a mate.

Often a communal life of this kind provides quite obvious advantages, for members of the herd who have particularly keen senses of smell, sight or hearing can be posted as sentries to keep watch and to warn the herd of the approach of danger. Penguins, which live together in groups, often post lookouts of this kind (bottom right).

A distinct branch of zoology has for some years past concerned itself with animal psychology. It has not limited itself entirely to the study of the behavior of individual animals, but has also studied the group behavior of animals which live in flocks or herds. Among other things, it has found that certain of these communities are by no means "classless societies". Some of them seem to recognize various degrees of status within the group. This is especially so among certain game birds and domestic fowls.

Some members of the group, by the way in which they strike defensive attitudes and by the way in which they make various pointing gestures with their beaks, seem to claim precedence over the others. Often they are given precedence, too, not only at feeding time but also when the birds seek a resting place and go to roost.

Fairly large groups of grazing animals sometimes put themselves under the direction of a leader whom they all follow blindly. Elephants, for example, usually live in herds led by an old female or occasionally by an old male. The leader often justifies its position by exercising considerable vigilance and keeping the herd out of danger. But if it becomes ill-tempered and savage, perhaps as a result of illness or accident, the whole herd may become dangerous and destroy everything in its path.

Many kinds of fish, too, live in shoals, including herring (bottom left). When one of their number has been seized and devoured by an enemy the others quickly flee from the spot, even if they have not seen the incident. At the moment it is bitten, the victim's skin exudes a material which, even when extremely diluted, has the effect of producing a veritable panic among the rest of the shoal. Although this material has been of no use to the victim, it has protected the rest of the community.

Many insects also live in communities, but their communal life is far more complex. Often they form societies where the division of labor is carried to a high degree of development.

Certain Siamese baboons live in groups of several families. The elephant herd follows a leader. A whole shoal of herring may be saved by one wounded member. Penguins make use of lookouts.

Insect Builders, Hoarders and Farmers

It is among the social insects that communal living has reached its highest pitch. Over many centuries man himself has learned, often by a painful process of trial and error, to live in larger and larger communities — the family, the tribe, the village, the town, the state. Slowly, reason and experience have taught him that it is worth curtailing some of his freedom of action and obeying a code of law in order to enjoy the benefits of such an organized way of living. Yet, by and large, he retains as much individual freedom as he can. Among the social insects, it is instinct, not reason, that decides on the communal way of life. The good of the community invariably comes before the good of any individual member.

In some insect communities, each member is destined throughout life to fulfill only one special task. This is particularly true of the wood-boring termites, or white ants, whose ravages — as the illustration shows — can bring about the destruction of a timber house.

Among the termites, division of labor has given rise to specialized insects which look so different from each other that one might easily believe them to be members of different species. Our illustration shows four members of a termite community: (A) the giant queen, (B) the king, (C) a sickle-jawed soldier, (D) a worker.

The queen is the hub of the termite nest. Around her its life revolves. She develops into little more than an unbelievably efficient egg-laying machine. Her body distended like a balloon, she may live as long as ten years, producing eggs at a steady rate of over 40,000 a day. In a single month her family is over a million strong. The king's place is at her side, his function to ensure that she lays fertile eggs. Around the royal pair a ring of soldiers stand guard. The many thousand workers are busy finding food and raising a great castle-like pinnacle of mud — often much higher than a man — to house the ever-growing population of termites.

Their enormous nest makes termites unique. But their highly organized way of life is also common to the ants we see in the U.S. Under the mound of pine needles that marks a wood ants' nest, egg-laying and the care of larvae are also specialized tasks carried out by queens and workers, in special chambers excavated for the purpose. If danger threatens, workers seize the helpless pupae and try to carry them to safety, at whatever risk to themselves.

The workers are sexless, but many of the pupae which they tend will later emerge as young winged queens and kings. On a warm summer's day the air is sometimes thick with flying ants. This is the young ants' wedding flight. Soon after it has taken place, the males die; the queens lose their wings and either enter an established nest or found a new one.

The world over, there are many kinds of ant communities working for their common good in many different ways. Some are hunters, others farmers. One American species actually keeps living honey-pots. Our illustration (middle right) shows them hanging from the ceiling of a nest. These honey-pots are really young ants, crammed by older ants with honey until their abdomens swell and serve as pitchers. They are living larders for their fellows.

The bottom left-hand picture shows red ants herding greenfly as we herd cattle. They will drive the greenfly into their ant hill and keep them there to be "milked" of the sweet liquid they secrete. There are other ants which bite off bits of green leaf and strew them over the floor of their nest to form a "field" in which to grow a small fungus as food.

Some insects even use tools of a kind. The ants shown at bottom right can stitch leaves together, using their own cocoons as needle and thread.

TOP: Termite ravages and members of termite community. CENTER: Wood ant nest and ants which serve as honey-pots. BOTTOM: Ants which herd greenfly and ants that stitch leaves together.

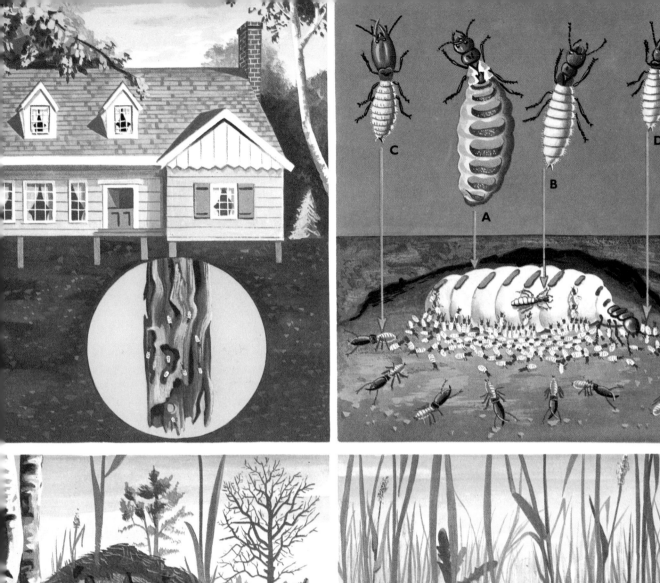

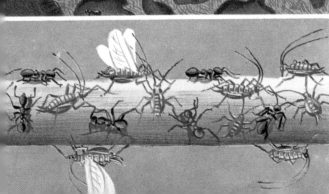

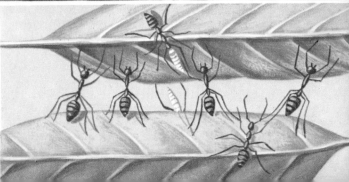

Cities Made
of Wax and Paper

Bumble bees found new communities each year. In spring, a female which has survived the rigors of winter will make a small, ball-like structure of moss and plant fibers, pierced by a single entrance hole, as shown opposite. If you could peer into the ball (top center) you would see that it contains several little oval cells made of wax and resin. In each of these cells the queen bumble bee lays eggs. They hatch into larvae which soon turn into adult bees.

Unlike the queen, their mother, these first bumble bees of the new season will never develop into females able to lay eggs. With only a poor food supply, they grow into somewhat stunted workers. They help to enlarge the nest, ready for the laying of more eggs. They also find food for the larvae which hatch from those eggs.

By summertime, when the nest is well staffed with nurses and breadwinners, the late-hatched larvae are well supplied with food. They will reach full maturity as fertile male and female bees. Later, after mating time, the males die, but many females survive until next spring. Then the founding of communities begins all over again.

The picture at the top right shows that even a fully developed bumble bee's nest is a relatively small affair. Each oval cell contains only two or three larvae (shown magnified). Much bigger, is the city of the honey bee, which may hold tens of thousands of inhabitants. Today, almost all honey bee hives that we see are, like the one pictured opposite, made by man. Honey bees seem to take readily to the arrangement whereby man provides them with comfortable, ready-made living quarters set in flower-filled fields and orchards, in return for a share of the honey they produce.

Like termites, different honey bees have different shapes according to the part they play within the community. The center illustration shows a long-bodied female (left), a big, solid-bodied male (below) and a smaller worker bee (right).

As in a termite colony, the queen lays the eggs, while the males do little more than ensure that they are fertile. While the queen is still laying her eggs, the young workers begin by taking on the "household chores". They clean the hive, produce wax to build the six-sided cells which serve as honey stores and nurseries, and they also tend and feed the larvae. After serving their indoor apprenticeship, the workers fly outside, collecting pollen and nectar. Pollen contains proteins — a vital part of the diet of the growing larvae. Nectar, transformed and stored as honey, is an energy-rich food. The larvae, properly fed and cared for, become adult insects in three weeks.

As bees multiply, their hive may no longer hold them all. Like the overgrown ameba, it splits in two. The old queen flies off, followed by a swarm of workers, and all settle on a tree. Left to themselves, these bees would build a new nest of their own; but usually a bee-keeper spots the swarm and transfers it to an empty man-made hive. The bees which remain in the old hive carry on as before, a young queen taking the place of the old one.

Bees' nests may last several years, but wasps build a new one each spring. A female wasp makes the first chambers of the palace from slivers of wood which she chews into a sort of paper. As the summer progresses, young wasps, developed from the eggs she lays there, add new paper cells, and the nest eventually takes on the shape you see in the bottom pictures.

Wasps have a notoriously sweet tooth for ripe fruit, but unlike honey bees, they do not store up honey for the winter. In autumn, all but the queens die. Next spring these begin nest-building again from scratch. Thus even the largest of wasp nests — and some grow as big as footballs — are the work of a single summer.

TOP: Bumble bees and their nest. CENTER: Honey bees at a man-made hive and (right) swarming. BOTTOM: A wasp nest as it appears from outside and (right) cut open to show its intricate construction.

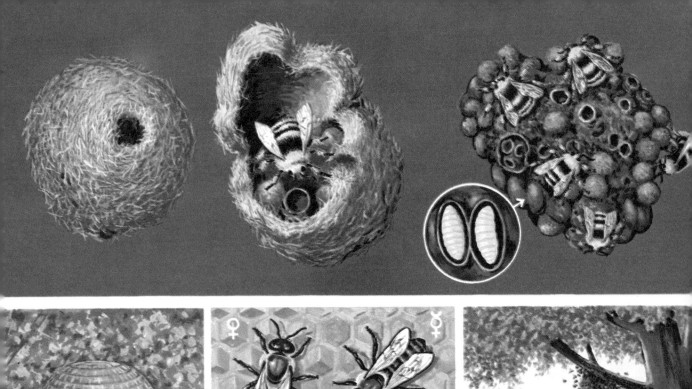

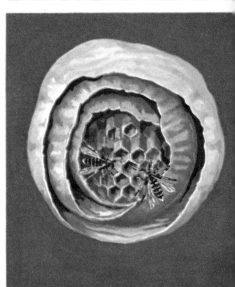

Plants and the Company they Keep

It is tempting to think of a big oak woods or a great pine forest as the plant world's equivalent of a community of social insects. But this is not so. Many members of one species of ant live together and work together for the mutual benefit of all. Though many oak trees may live together, each grows quite independently of its neighbors.

However, there are good reasons why trees of the same species often grow together in large numbers. Soil and climate are the main factors which decide where different trees grow, and often, over large areas, both soil and climate favor the growth of only one or two species. The type of tree which grows on a sandy heath differs from that which grows in clay meadows. Pine forests flourish to the very fringe of the Arctic while palm trees thrive only in or near the tropics.

In the U.S., a mountain top seldom produces more than a few stunted trees. Yet thick woods may clothe the valleys a mere mile away. In effect, mountain tops experience a microclimate of their own, quite different from that of the valleys. But over most of the U.S., soil plays a greater part than climate in determining the natural vegetation. On alkaline, chalk downland, beech trees may dominate the landscape. On acid, sandy heathland, pine trees may make a thick umbrella stretching for several miles. On clay lowland soils, oak woods are common.

In a forest of densely-packed pine trees, few smaller plants really flourish, largely because little sunlight can filter through to the forest floor. But in mixed open woodland, where soils vary and support several different kinds of tree, many plants of different species flourish in the partial shade. Our bottom picture shows an example. Below the great tree-trunks grow shrubs like the flowering yellow broom and dogwood, and tall plants like the foxglove. Then comes a lower layer of sprawling blackberries, ferns (which thrive in shady spots) and grasses. The lowest layer of all includes fungi, which do not need sunlight to manufacture their food, and also mosses.

Though they do not benefit each other directly, like members of an insect community, all these plants are adapted to living successfully with their neighbors. In fact, if you chopped down the shade-giving trees, ferns and fungi would no longer thrive.

A woodland community is but one example of living arrangements reached by different plants in habitats varying from a wayside ditch to a tropical jungle. Beside a ditch, certain tiny plants manage to live successfully with taller ones which shut out sunlight. Low-flowering violets adapted to this way of life bloom in early spring before tall-growing grasses and hedge-parsley grow up and hem them in.

Ever since man became a tiller of the soil, he has aimed at keeping his cultivated fields "pure" plant communities, consisting only of the plants he wishes to grow. He has certainly decided which grasses shall dominate his cornfield. He has bred them over many centuries, using judicious selection to produce the cultivated grasses, or cereals, whose seeds are pictured opposite: (A) oats, (B) corn (C) barley, (D) rye, (E) wheat and (F) spelt, or German wheat.

Yet even a cornfield still remains a mixed community. Among the wheat flourish many other plants which we call weeds. The top left illustration shows that beneath the waving ears of a cornfield lurk a host of other plants growing in association with the dominant species. There are poppies, mayweed, coltsfoot, cornflowers and many others which vary according to the soil on which the wheat is growing.

Even where man's buildings almost obliterate the living landscape, a botanist can tell what plants would grow together if the bricks and concrete were removed. He can see only a handful of tiny plants which have sprung up on the few bare patches of soil. Yet from them he can describe the whole vegetable community of which, in nature, they would form a part.

TOP LEFT: Nature's plant community within a cornfield. TOP RIGHT: Six cereals which man has bred to dominate his fields. BELOW: A plant community in open woodland.

Plants which Grow from Tubers and Spores

Nothing lives forever. Whether the life-span of an organism is only a few hours, like that of some single-cell creatures, or hundreds of years, like that of a giant redwood tree, it must die eventually. Often, too, some accident or the attacks of its natural enemies may bring a living organism to a premature end. If plants and animals were not adequately equipped to reproduce their own species, life on earth would cease. Yet earth's myriad living things are so tenacious of life that they have evolved not one but many ways of perpetuating the species.

As we saw on page 17, animals like the single-cell ameba reproduce simply by splitting in two. Each of the resulting daughter cells is a complete animal able to lead an independent life. Certain multi-cell animals, like the freshwater hydra, can reproduce by growing buds which develop into separate, fully-formed animals. Among animals, reproduction without sex is confined to species not very high in the evolutionary scale. But among plants it is common even in highly-developed species.

The top left-hand picture shows a strawberry plant which is multiplying by "layering". The parent plant throws out a shoot which grows outward and downward. Where it touches the soil, it sends down roots from which a new plant begins to grow. In time the gardener can snap the "lifeline" between the new plant and the old one without harming either. Later he can safely replant the new one in another strawberry bed if he wishes to.

The pictures just below that of the strawberry show three stages in the life of a potato. The part of the potato plant which we eat, or a so-called "seed potato", is a tuber — a swollen underground part of the stem containing a reserve supply of food. From its "eyes" sprout shoots which grow into the stem and roots of a new plant. By the time it has produced a complete new plant, the old potato is soft and shriveled. Biologists refer to propagation of new plants from part of an old one as vegetative reproduction.

The fungi shown opposite reproduce in yet another way. The underground network of root-like threads pushes a fruiting "cap" above ground, the underside of which contains a large number of tiny spores. Spores are cells, or small groups of cells, specialized to perform the task of creating a new living organism.

When the fruiting cap is ripe, these light-weight spores are blown far and wide by the wind, many of them lodging in the earth and sending out new networks of underground threads.

It is amazing just how many spores of various kinds of fungi are present in the air. If, almost anywhere, you leave a slice of bread in a damp place for a few days, spores will have settled on it and produced a fine velvety layer of mold. Different species of molds also settle and grow quickly on cheese which is left uncovered.

Since spores are carried to new growing ground so easily, and give rise to great increases in the numbers of a species, it is no wonder that so many widespread plants are spore-bearers. Seaweeds, moss and ferns — all spore-bearers — are among the world's oldest plants. They flourished millions of years before the first flowering plants appeared. In the great forests of the far-off Coal Age, spore-bearing plants far outnumbered all others.

Beneath the tiger lily's flowers (bottom left), small, dark swellings form where the leaves sprout from the stem. These swellings are filled with structures from which the plant can reproduce vegetatively. Yet the tiger lily is a flowering plant and, as we shall shortly see, flowering plants have their own special methods of reproduction. Thus the tiger lily plays safe. It possesses two ways of multiplying.

TOP LEFT: A new strawberry plant grows from a "runner". TOP RIGHT: How a potato-tuber gives rise to a new plant. BOTTOM LEFT: The tiger lily, which has two ways of reproducing. BOTTOM RIGHT: These fungi carry spores in their fleshy "caps".

Making Sure that Seeds are Fertile

There are many flowering shrubs and other plants which the gardener can grow from cuttings or "slips" taken from older plants. These are examples of vegetative reproduction. But in nature the majority of flowering plants multiply by a more complex process. They bear reproductive cells of different sexes. A male pollen grain must unite with a female ovule to produce a fertile seed which will grow into a new plant.

Many species carry both male and female reproductive cells on one and the same individual plant. Biologists call them monoecious plants, a name which comes from two Greek words meaning single and house. Their reproductive system is self-contained, for within its own single household, a monoecious plant possesses the means of multiplication.

Catkins are the monoecious hazel's male flowers. On a catkin-bearing hazel you will also find the female flowers, though these are tiny, red-tipped outgrowths on the twigs. Some monoecious plants like the buttercup (top left) combine male and female cells in a single flower. The illustration shows the male stamens (as a red ring) surrounding the female pistil (colored blue). Magnified are the stalk of the male stamen and its anther which holds sacs containing the fertilizing pollen grains. The female pistil (also shown magnified) includes the ovary, containing the ovules or unfertilized seeds, and the stigma, or surface which receives the pollen.

Dioecious plants (from two Greek words meaning two houses) also bear male and female reproductive cells but not both on one plant. Somehow these different cells, which may be on plants many yards apart, must be brought together to produce a fertilized seed. Either the wind or insects may carry pollen to the female ovule. Plants which depend on insects often have large, brightly colored flowers which act as signals to attract their useful guests. These guests feed on nectar deep inside the flowers and then, all unknowingly, ferry the pollen to other plants of the same species.

A well-known dioecious plant is "palm" or sallow. Its flowers open at the very end of winter when there are few others to tempt the early bees. The sallow depends almost entirely on insect pollination because its male and female flowers grow on separate plants. Our illustrations (below) show the flowers of both sexes with a close-up view of each.

Flowering plants are often equipped with ingenious means of securing pollination by insects. A familiar plant provides a good example of such ingenuity. This is the arum lily (center of opposite page) also called "lords and ladies" and "cuckoo-pint". Early in spring, it grows rapidly in warm, shady hedgerows, thrusting up a long spike sheathed in a pale green spathe.

The spike, tainted by an unpleasant smell, attracts many tiny insects. These insects adventure down the spike into the sheath. They push easily through a ring of down-curved bristles (pictured at the center right of the facing page), brushing past the stamens. But these stamens are not yet mature, and are not yet bearing pollen. So the insects carry down to the ovules of the plant only the pollen which they have brought from some other arum lily. The insects drink the nectar they find at the bottom of the spathe and turn to fly away.

A shock awaits them, for the down-curved bristles which made the way in seem so easy, are of course up-curved on the way out. These bristles now hold them prisoner. For a day or so they are trapped. Then the arum lily's stamens ripen and cover the insects with pollen. At the same time, the bristles shrivel and release them. None the wiser, they soon fly to another arum lily, fertilize it, and again find themselves in prison for a spell.

Thus the monoecious arum lily behaves like a dioecious plant. It attracts pollen-carrying insects and its elaborate insect-trap ensures cross-pollination — a device which leads to stronger new plants than those produced when monoecious plants fertilize themselves.

TOP: The monoecious buttercup. CENTER: The arum lily, and its elaborate trap for pollen-carrying insects. BOTTOM: The dioecious sallow. In all these diagrams red shows male parts; blue, female.

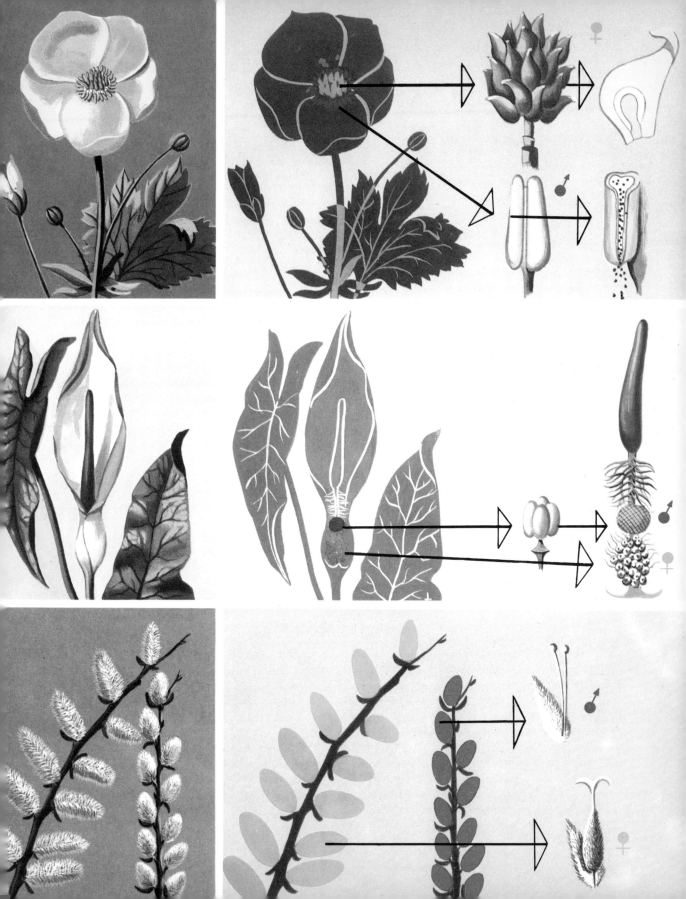

One Becomes Many, Two Make One

We have had a brief look at asexual (one-becomes-many) and sexual (two-make-one) reproduction among plants. Some plants and some animals use both asexual and sexual methods of reproduction, in alternate generations. One of the best known plants to do so is the fern, shown at (A) in the upper part of the facing illustration.

We have already noticed that the fern is a spore-bearer. The underside of a mature fern leaf, at certain times, becomes studded with little reddish-brown patches, shown at (B). These are sporangia — organs in which spores are asexually produced. If you place one of them, as circled at (C), under the microscope, you will see it as shown at (D), though its real size is no greater than that of a grain of sand.

Greatly magnified, at (E), is a picture of what happens when the sporangium bursts open and frees the minute spores. Drifting on a puff of wind, any one of these spores may lodge in damp soil. There, as shown at (F), it develops into a small disc which attaches itself to the soil by a number of minute "hairs". Soon it becomes the heart-shaped prothallus (G). A powerful microscope reveals that there are two little bumps on it, shown at (G) and (H). These bumps are microscopic male and female sex organs. In warm weather, the male organ releases male reproductive cells — tiny corkscrew-shaped bodies which can thresh themselves along through water by means of fine, lashing threads. They swim over the surface of the prothallus, in even the slightest trace of moisture, until they reach the female reproductive cells. Then they pierce the sticky outer covering of the female cell and unite with it. From this union grows a tiny new fern.

This means that ferns employ both asexual and sexual reproduction at different stages of their life cycle. The mature fern gives rise to spores asexually. The spore, its offspring, gives rise to a new fern by sexual reproduction.

In the animal world, the liver-fluke provides another instance of a living thing that reproduces both sexually and asexually. The bottom illustration shows the life cycle of this small, flattish worm — a parasite which preys on sheep and water snails.

Adult liver-flukes live inside a sheep's bile-duct or liver where they can cause serious illness and even death. Eggs laid by the liver-fluke pass out from the sheep's body with its droppings (1). If an egg falls in a farm ditch or brook, it hatches into a swimming larva (2). This young larva swims about until it can attach itself to a water snail (3). It finds its way inside the snail where, in time, it develops into a sporocyst, a tiny cyst or bladder in which spores are produced asexually (4). These spores develop into larvae called rediae (5). The skin of the sporocyst bursts open and releases the rediae; then, still inside the snail, they also reproduce asexually to form yet other larvae called cercariae (6).

The tadpole-like, free-swimming cercariae leave the snail and fasten themselves to a blade of grass or to some other meadow plant. There they cover themselves with a membrane (7), and stay until such time as a sheep eats the plant. In the sheep's intestine the cercariae become freed from their outer membrane and find their way to the sheep's liver or bile-duct. There they grow into fully adult worms (8) which reproduce sexually, giving rise to the eggs from which the life cycle begins all over again.

Thus the story of the liver-fluke covers four separate stages, of which three involve asexual reproduction and only the fourth sexual reproduction. The life cycle of this lowly parasite is an amazing example of nature's ingenious methods of ensuring the survival of a species.

The illustrations show the life cycles of a plant and an animal which multiply by both sexual and asexual means. ABOVE: The common fern. BELOW: The liver-fluke.

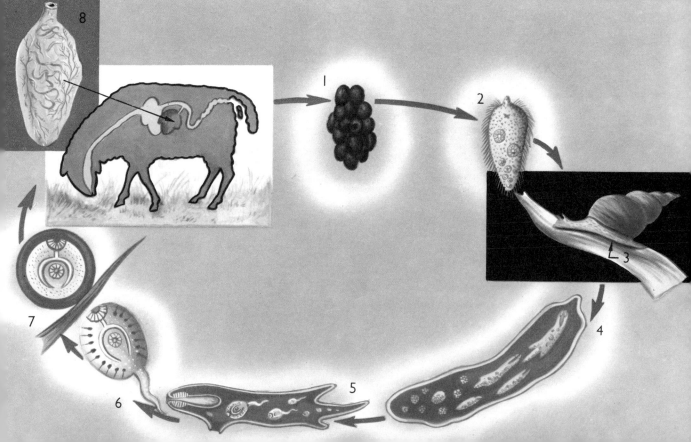

Courtship and Finery in the Animal World

In the great majority of species of higher animal, male and female each has its own indispensable part to play in reproduction. Yet, for a great part of their lives, the male and the female may live quite independently of each other, each seeking food and resting in different places. Somehow some of them will have to come together at least at mating time and for at least as long as their joint efforts are needed to care for and tend their young ones.

Such meetings are facilitated by making use of the creatures' senses to attract each other. Thus males may attract females, or females may attract males, by signals of sound, scent or sight — and even by appealing to senses which man does not possess and does not fully understand. Just as the medieval knight jousted and tilted before the lady of his choice, so do many males of the animal kingdom seek to impress the chosen female by displaying their strength and courage. Just as the fine ladies and gentlemen of Regency days donned splendid clothes to attract and impress one another, so do many of nature's creatures display their finest garb at the time of their wooing.

Among many species of bird, fish and mammal, it is the male which is most active in attracting a partner. Often he does it by some sort of visual display. In nature, as we have seen, colors often serve as camouflage. But a bird of paradise could scarcely be inconspicuous against any natural background. The plumage of the male (upper bird in the bottom left-hand picture) is not designed to hide its wearer but to make it attractive to the female. To show off his plumage to best advantage, he displays before her in a ritual set of movements. This is one of many instances in which birds have developed brightly colored plumage and a nuptial "dance" as a set of signals to attract a mate.

Nuptial displays are not restricted to the bird world. Anyone who has kept tropical fish will recognize similar signals in the swordtail. Our illustration (top right) shows a male and female green swordtail — the wild type from the inland waters of southern Mexico. This fish gets its name from a secondary sex characteristic — the "sword" which the male alone possesses.

Like the swords of honor which noblemen wear on ceremonial occasions, it serves no practical purpose. Indeed, the "sword" is merely a flexible extension of the tail fin, serving only to impress the ladies. A courting swordtail displays himself before his mate, darting around her from all angles, no doubt partly to show off this splendid ornament.

Today we are accustomed to seeing hornless sheep — the product of man's artificial selection exercised over many years of sheep-breeding. But most wild rams, like the domesticated one pictured bottom right, are horned. The ram's horns, like the swordtail's "sword", are a secondary sex characteristic. But a ram's horns can be useful as well as decorative. They make very effective weapons in a fight for possession of ewes.

A ewe is less likely to be attracted by the ram with the most impressive horns than to submit to whichever ram can rout its rivals in battle. Thus, though ram's horns do not directly help to bring the sexes together, they do further nature's purpose. They help the strongest ram to conquer, and the victorious ram mates with the ewes and hands on his strength to future generations.

Some animals possess secondary sex characteristics which, unlike any so far described, play a part in actual mating. Both sexes of the water beetle shown in the top left-hand picture have developed quite distinctive features. The male has smooth, shiny wing cases while the female's back is heavily ridged. The male, unlike the female, has tiny cushions on its hind legs which serve as suction caps. At mating time, the male clasps the female with its hind legs, its suction caps gripping firmly on to her ridged back.

TOP LEFT: A male and female water beetle. RIGHT: Green swordtails. BOTTOM LEFT: Birds of paradise. BOTTOM RIGHT: Horned ram and hornless ewe.

Fierce Battles Between Male Rivals

Some of the fiercest battles between animals arise out of rivalry among males for possession of the females of the species. Few are fiercer than those which occur among the red deer.

Nature has equipped the stags, which poets have described as monarchs of the forest, with formidable weapons — great branching antlers whose branches grow in number year by year. In autumn each stag begins collecting a number of hinds together and starts to issue throaty challenges to any rival that may be close by. Soon a fierce duel begins between two rival stags. Usually it ends when one succeeds in driving the other away, but sometimes the winner gores the loser so badly that it dies. It is even known for the battle to continue until both stags are locked in death by one another's antlers.

Often a series of such battles rages close by the watching hinds. For a time the final conqueror does indeed become king of the whole herd, and veritable monarch of the forest. But his reign is short-lived. It lasts only for the comparatively short period of mating.

Once the mating season ends, the stag loses all interest in the hinds as they do in him. Soon he sheds his impressive antlers, and spends a great part of the year looking rather like a big thickset hind. Not until the following summer do new and even grander antlers grow again.

At no time does the stag show any interest in his offspring. Their care is the sole responsibility of their mothers. Hinds not only care for their fawns in their first few months of life, but may continue to look after them for two or more years. Throughout that period, and, indeed, throughout their lives, the young females will live among a herd made up entirely of hinds. This herd has a permanent leader, herself an old, experienced hind.

Only in the rutting season does this herd attach itself to a stag. For the rest of the time the stags either live a solitary life or roam the forest in small all-male communities. But unlike the well-organized herds of hinds, these groups of stags seem to have no commonly accepted leader.

Rivalry between males extends throughout the animal kingdom, under water as well as on the dry land. Most of us have heard of the fierce rivalry of male Siamese fighting fish, yet those who have kept just one of these creatures in an aquarium can scarcely believe these stories. Resplendent in his flowing fins and gorgeous colors, a single "fighter" may lead a perfectly peaceful life, swimming quite unconcerned among the other species of fish which share the same tank. But put another male fighting fish in with him and see the difference. Both males suddenly seem to glow with even deeper, brighter colors and their fins begin to bristle. At first they swim slowly side by side and one might even think they were making friends. But they are sizing each other up, like two boxers circling for an opening.

Suddenly the battle begins. There is a quick blur of color and one male has struck. Then both are weaving around one another, striking repeated blows. Soon, their fins are torn to ribbons by each other's tiny, sharp teeth.

In Siam, the country of their origin, people once staged combats between these fish, wagering on which would win. Confined in a glass bowl with no way of escape, the vanquished often lost his life in losing the fight. However, if you keep a fighter and want to see his battle colors without witnessing their destruction, you have only to place a mirror against the glass of the aquarium. The fighter mistakes his reflection for a rival and parades before it in all his finery.

A terrible foe, the fighter is nevertheless an exemplary father. He blows a bubble nest where he looks after the eggs which the female lays. When they hatch, he guards the young against their many enemies.

ABOVE: Rival red deer stags in combat, watched by a group of hinds. BELOW: Male Siamese fighting fish making ready for battle.

How Eggs and Seeds are Fertilized

Remarkable though it may seem, it is less than ninety years ago that scientists first had any real understanding of what fertilization involves. The reproductive cells, or gametes — which are strikingly similar among a vast number of species — were not discovered until the end of the seventeenth century, by the Dutchman, Van Leeuwenhoek, pioneer of the microscope. It was not then seen very clearly what practical purpose this discovery might serve. Not until much later was it understood that all representatives of the animal kingdom, human beings included, produce eggs and that this characteristic is not peculiar to birds and fishes.

Mammals' eggs were first discovered in 1827, but it was not until 1875 that the respective roles of these eggs and of spermatozoa, or male reproductive cells, were discovered. With the intuition characteristic of the great naturalists, Van Leeuwenhoek had firmly suggested that the spermatozoon must penetrate to the inside of the egg. On the strength of this suggestion certain later scientists examined various fertilized eggs under the microscope, and they did from time to time see the tail of a spermatozoon in the plasma. But this was the limit of their discoveries.

Then in 1875, two German scientists, the Hertwig brothers, succeeded in actually observing the fertilization of sea-urchins' eggs. Before that time the most divergent opinions had been expressed on the subject of the male and female reproductive cells and of the part they played in reproduction. Some people thought that the egg was the procreator of the new organism. Others believed that the spermatozoon contained, quite ready, but in an extremely tiny form, the new organism and that the egg merely served as a nursery and food supply for it.

The Hertwig brothers now mixed together the eggs and the sperms of sea-urchins and with the help of microscopes, actually watched what happened during fertilization. A number of spermatozoa (illustration A) with large "heads" and long, lashing tails (which made them look very much like certain single-cell water creatures) advanced towards the eggs. They attached themselves to the membrane of the latter, attempting to pierce it. At the moment the spermatozoon succeeded in forcing an entry, the head separated from the tail, which became useless (B). Only the head penetrated the plasma of the egg. At the same time, the egg formed a thin membrane which prevented the entry of any other spermatozoa or male gametes.

Once it is inside the egg, the head of the spermatozoon — which is a special kind of cell-nucleus — absorbs some of the egg's plasma and begins to grow (C). A few minutes after the beginning of fertilization the nucleus of the spermatozoon has reached the same size as the nucleus of the egg. These two nuclei move towards each other and, coming into contact, form a single new nucleus. The nucleus of the unfertilized egg, like the nucleus of the spermatozoon, contains only an unpaired set of chromosomes. The fertilized egg, after union with the spermatozoon, contains a *paired* set. Fertilization is then accomplished, although much must still happen before a new living creature is formed.

Sexual reproduction of plants also involves the fusion of two cells. The process is shown in the upper part of the illustration, in stages numbered 1 to 8.

The pistil, or female part of the plant, is shown in section form (1), with the ovary containing the unfertilized seeds, or ovules, the stigma which receives the pollen, and the stalk-like style. The grains of pollen (2) — the male cells — are, by one means or another, brought in contact with the stigma (3). This pollen, after a certain time, starts to germinate and works its way down a passage formed in the style (4, 5). This passage enables the nucleus of the male cell (pollen) to approach the female cell, or ovule (6), then to reach it (7), and finally to penetrate it and join with it (8).

TOP: How pollen grains reach the ovules of a flower and join with them to form fertilized seeds. BOTTOM: How a spermatozoon enters an egg and fertilizes it.

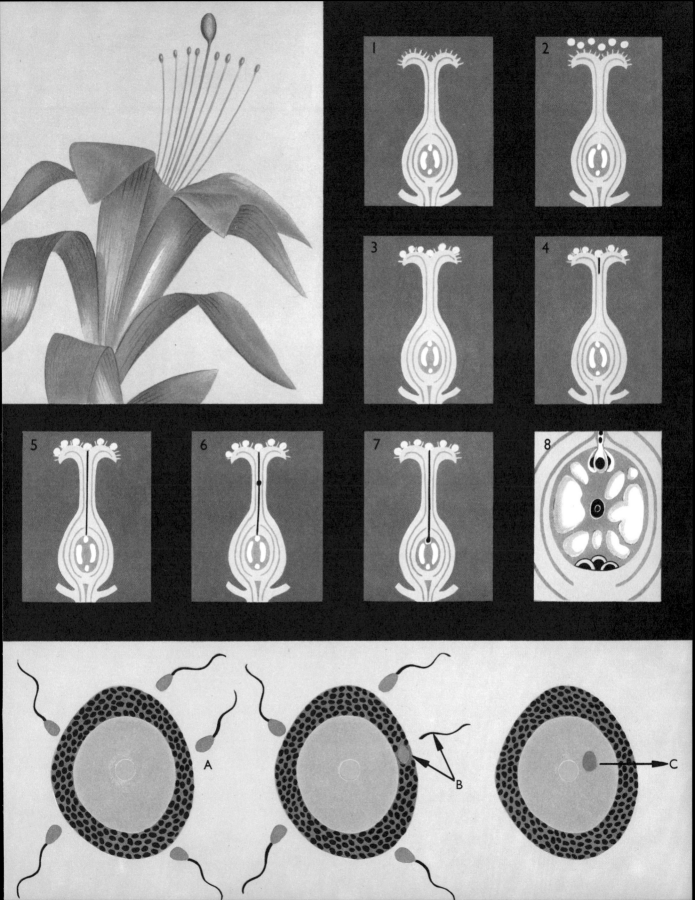

How Family Likenesses are Passed On

Family likenesses, both in animals and in the higher plants, are passed on from generation to generation by almost unbelievably small units called genes. Twenty thousand genes laid end to end would scarcely measure as much as a single millimeter, and every cell of an animal's body may contain a great number of them.

There are many different kinds of gene and each kind exercises its own special effect on the development of the individual who possesses it in his body-cells. Some genes affect one organ of the body, some another, and some doubtless affect several organs. Some have a very powerful effect, some a comparatively weak one. The great majority of the genes so far known to scientists occur in the chromosomes of cells, so we can safely say that the way in which chromosomes are passed on from one generation to another is the main circumstance which explains how family likenesses are passed on.

Very early on in this book we saw how, when a single-cell animal divides into two, the number of chromosomes in the original cell doubles first, and then exactly half of that total goes to each of the new daughter cells. Each new cell thus has precisely the same number of chromosomes as the parent cell originally possessed. We also saw that every species of animal and plant always has its own characteristic number of chromosomes in every body-cell.

In human beings the body-cells contain 46 chromosomes. But before a new human being can be formed two cells — one male and one female — must unite. If the female ovum and the male spermatozoon each contained 46 chromosomes, the fertilized ovum which is made up of both would contain 92. But it so happens that the gametes, or reproductive cells — both male and female — contain only half as many chromosomes as all the rest of the body-cells. So in human beings both the egg and the spermatozoon have 23 chromosomes each. The amazing thing about it is this. The ordinary body-cells are *diploid*, containing 23 *almost identical pairs* of chromosomes; the reproductive cells are *haploid*, containing 23 *single* chromosomes. Thus a fertilized ovum contains 23 chromosomes corresponding to those in the mother's body-cells and 23 corresponding to those in the father's body-cells. It thus contains all the essential hereditary characteristics of both parents.

The pictures on the right show how this works out over three generations. The father of the baby (center, left) has, in the ordinary cells of his body, one unpaired set of chromosomes from his father and one from his mother (the baby's paternal grandparents, shown top left). Some of these cells, instead of dividing like those we saw early in the book, divide in a rather more complicated way — by a process called meiosis. By this process (shown to the right of the man, in several stages) one ordinary cell eventually gives rise to 4 spermatozoa. Each still contains some chromosomes (blue) from the man's father, and some (red) from his mother.

In a similar way, the baby's mother also inherits, in her ordinary body-cells, chromosomes both from *her* father and *her* mother (the baby's maternal grandparents, shown top right). Again, by a slightly different process of meiosis (shown in the diagrams beside her), one of these gives rise to an ovum, or egg-cell, still containing chromosomes inherited from her father and mother.

When the spermatozoon and the ovum unite the resulting fertilized cell, from which the baby grows, therefore contains chromosomes from all four grandparents. It may happen that genes from one grandparent have an almost opposite effect to that produced by genes from one of the others, in which case one family likeness, at least, will be blurred.

Family likenesses are carried by chromosomes in the body cells. Because of the way these divide to form reproductive cells, a baby inherits chromosomes not merely from both parents, but also from all four grandparents.

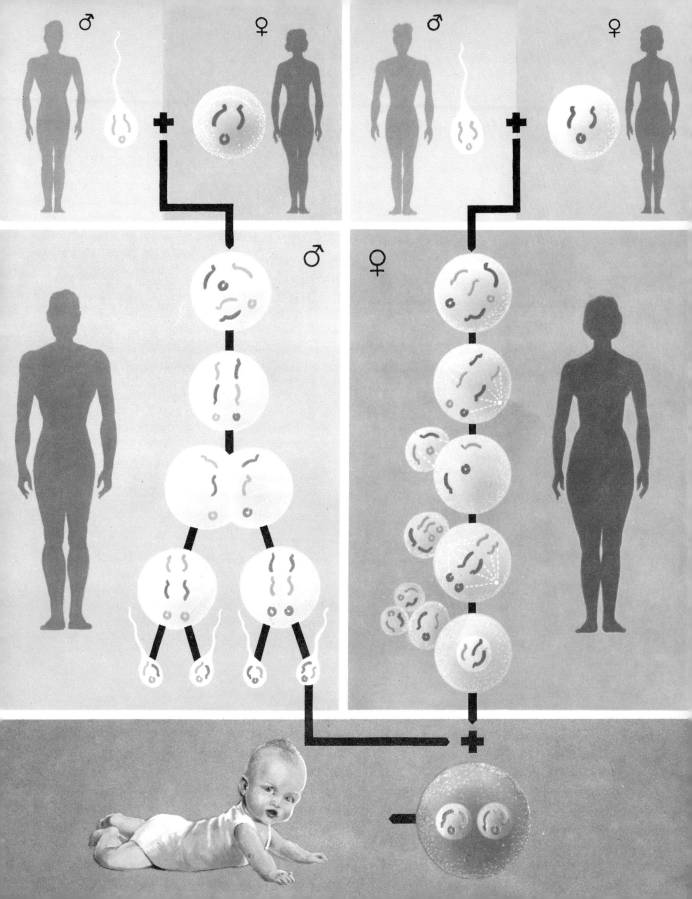

The Egg— Symbol of New Life

In ancient times there was no science as we know it today, but the ordinary man — the hunter, the fisherman, the herdsman or the farmer — lived in close contact with nature and was acutely conscious of many of her great miracles. Perhaps the one which took the firmest hold on his imagination was how new life springs from an egg.

The great Christian festival commemorating Christ's resurrection falls very near to the spring equinox, and to March 25th, which for several centuries was New Year's Day. In England it is named after Eostre, the Teutonic goddess of spring and reawakening life, and it has always been closely associated with eggs, the symbol of new life.

According to an old Finnish legend the very earth and heavens owe their beginnings to an egg. The story is that Ilmatar, Daughter of Nature, while resting on the waves of the primeval ocean, took pity on a wild goose which could find no resting place and allowed it to sit in her lap. There it laid eggs which in course of time fell into the water. They did not sink, but broke open and gave rise to the earth, the sun, the moon and the stars.

If we stop to consider what a wonderful thing an egg really is, early people's flights of fancy about it are scarcely surprising. When we think of a single living cell, we normally think of some minute thing which can be seen only with the aid of a microscope. Yet an egg — even the enormous egg of an ostrich — is but a single cell, marvelously adapted to the task of producing a new living creature.

The top right hand diagram gives some idea of how complex an ordinary hen's egg is. Just in-side the hard but porous protective outer shell (9) is a semitransparent membrane (7) which forms a kind of lining. Towards the "big end" is an air chamber (8), separated from the white, or albumen (4) by another membrane (6). Inside the albumen is the yellow mass of the yolk (3), the middle of which contains a layer of fat (2). Above the yolk is the germinal disc (1), the germinating point from which the young chick will begin to grow. However often the sitting hen may roll the egg over, this vital germinating point always remains uppermost, nearest the warmth of her body, owing to the special balancing devices in the egg (5).

Many classes of animals besides birds produce eggs: amphibians, reptiles, insects, mollusks (which include cockles, oysters, mussels, snails and octopuses), worms, echinoderms (which include starfishes and sea urchins) and mammals.

In the case of birds, and in the case of many fishes, the young creature which hatches from the egg is, or quickly becomes, very like its parents. But in many other instances the young creature which first comes from the egg bears little or no resemblance to its parents and looks nothing like it will look when it reaches the adult stage. This is true of many insects, such as moths and butterflies which begin life as caterpillars. It is also true of many amphibians, such as frogs, which begin life as tadpoles.

Most classes of animals lay their eggs before the embryo, or new living creature, begins to form. But there are exceptions. Some fishes, for instance, bring forth their young alive, the embryo having formed in the egg while it is still in the mother fish's body.

Almost all mammals are viviparous; that is, the embryo develops in the ovum which remains inside the mother's body, and is brought into the world as a fully formed living creature. But here, too, there are exceptions. The duckbilled platypus, a strange mammal which lives in Australia, lays eggs just as amphibians and reptiles do, though it later feeds its young ones with milk.

TOP LEFT: Reminder of an old legend which attributes the origin of the universe to an egg. TOP RIGHT: Inside a hen's egg. BELOW: How a fish, a frog, a chicken and a horse develop from eggs.

Young Ones Quite Unlike their Parents

Newly-born mammals and newly-hatched birds have much the same shape and structure as their parents. A kitten is obviously a small cat, a puppy a small dog, a duckling a small duck. But, as we have already noticed, this is not so throughout the whole of the animal kingdom. In many instances newly-hatched living creatures bear little or no resemblance to their parents and must undergo drastic changes of shape and structure before they reach the adult stage. In such instances the initial stage of life is called the larval stage.

Some larvae are so different from their parents that larva and adult have often, in the past, been mistaken for two quite different species. It must have taken early men very many generations to realize that the crawling caterpillar is the young one of the beautiful flying moth or butterfly, and that the swimming tadpole is the young one of the jumping frog. Until even comparatively recent times men were unaware that the small sea creatures shown to the left of the crab on the opposite page are actually young crabs themselves.

Everything in nature has a reason, and these surprising differences between parents and young ones are no exception. Many sea-dwelling animals, in the adult stage, are sedentary creatures, living fixed in one place or moving only rarely over small distances. Mussels, sea-urchins and barnacles are examples. If their young ones were exactly like themselves these species would each have to live forever in one vast and ever-growing mass. But in fact their larvae are all free-swimming creatures, able to move away and settle down elsewhere when they change into adults.

Again, many amphibians spend much of their adult lives on land, and are equipped with limbs. Yet their soft eggs, if laid and left on land, would dry out and never hatch. In fact they lay their eggs in water, and the young ones which hatch out are swimming creatures before they undergo the drastic change, or metamorphosis, by which they, too, become land-dwellers.

The pictures opposite show stages by which six different larvae develop into adults: top left, a butterfly; top right, a beetle; center left, a fly; center right, a moth; next two pictures, a crab; bottom strip of pictures, a grasshopper. Though there are similarities, the process differs in each case.

The larvae of the butterfly, the beetle, the fly and the moth are all wingless. They must all, therefore, live quite a different kind of life from the winged adults, but each is capable, meanwhile, of fending for itself and finding its own food. But before becoming an adult, each of them goes through an intermediate stage as a pupa. When the larva becomes a pupa it can no longer feed or move about. But tremendous changes of shape and structure are going on while it is in this apparently lifeless state, and it emerges as a winged adult. The pictures show that the larva of the fly, unlike the rest, is legless, and all four pupae differ considerably from one another. That of the beetle, for instance, is far more like the adult form than that of the fly.

The larvae of crabs undergo less drastic changes. The picture shows two larval forms. At each, the young crab possesses limbs and organs very much like those of the adult, and the changes at the various stages of development are, in the main, merely changes of appearance.

The life-story of the grasshopper presents quite a different picture. The larva is already like the adult, except that it is smaller and has no wings, but only short stumps. It also leads the same kind of life. In the course of development it goes through no pupal stage. Instead it simply grows bigger, shedding its old skin five times and growing a new and larger one each time. Only after the last molt do its wings appear, but they then grow rapidly.

TOP: Larvae, pupae and adult forms of four insects: butterfly, beetle, fly and moth. CENTER: Two larval forms and adult form of crab. BOTTOM: Stages in development of a grasshopper.

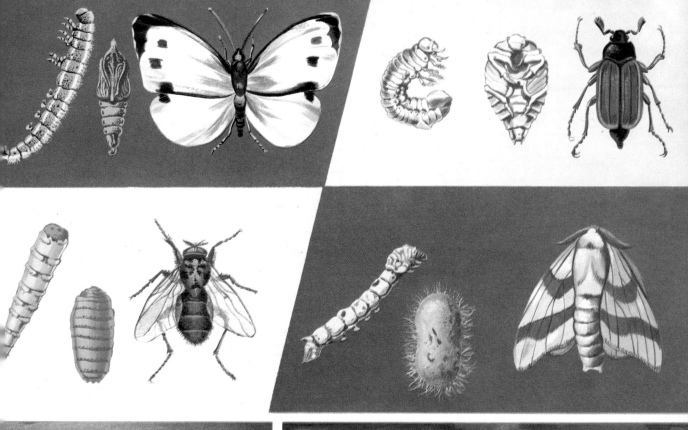

Birds as Domestic Architects

The amount of care and attention which different kinds of animals give to their young ones varies enormously. A herring may lay as many as forty thousand eggs a year but very few of them give rise to new fishes. They are left quite unprotected in the water and the vast majority are eaten by other sea creatures. Skates and rays, on the other hand, lay very few eggs. Each egg, already fertilized before it is laid, is encased in what looks like a small semi-transparent envelope, and contains a rich supply of yolk to feed the young fish which will develop inside it. Most of the few eggs which the skate lays give rise to new fishes, and by the time the young ones hatch out they are able to swim about and find food for themselves.

There are similar wide differences in parental care among insects. We have already seen how much care bees and ants lavish on their larvae. Yet many other insects, including crane-flies, butterflies, grasshoppers and mayflies, simply lay their eggs and leave them. The only care they seem to take is to lay the eggs where, when the young ones hatch out, they can find food.

It is among birds, perhaps, that care for the young is most widespread and general. True, the cuckoo leaves to other birds the hatching of its eggs and rearing of its fledglings, but the great majority of birds begin working for their young ones even before they lay their eggs, and go on caring for them until they are well able to take care of themselves. The first step most birds take is to build a nest, and often the male bird shoulders the greater part of this work.

Just as among primitive peoples each tribe builds its own characteristic type of shelter, so among birds each species has its own style of domestic architecture. The bower bird of Australia and New Guinea, shown in the top picture, builds a cradle-like nest among low branches. Quite unadorned it would serve as a satisfactory place to lay and hatch eggs. But the bower bird is not content with mere utility. Just in front of the nest it builds an arch-like bower of twigs which it decorates with brightly-colored flowers, pebbles, shells and feathers. Often it adds similar decorations to the nest itself.

Swallows (center left) build their saucer-shaped nests of three "traditional" building materials — mud, dry grass and feathers — and are usually careful to choose a place where the nest is well protected, such as a chimney stack or a corner of a barn. The South African tit (center right) in bygone times used to build itself a nest of moss, but today it has profited from the appearance of large flocks of sheep in the country. It has deserted its old building material and now builds with wool. The finished nest looks as if it were cut out of felt.

The tropical bird shown in the bottom center picture makes its nest from pieces of fiber, dead leaves and other dried materials, the whole being held together with fine threads taken from spiders' webs. Hung from the end of a branch, the finished structure looks rather like a coconut with a slit covered by a kind of porch roof. Inside the nest, which is well concealed among leaves, young birds are almost completely hidden from any possible enemies. Certain birds which live in East Asia make very similar nests (bottom left), but use finer building materials. These nests, too, have an opening at the side, but they have no "porch roof".

One of the most remarkable nests of all is that made by the tailor birds of India and China. With their sharp beaks these birds make a series of holes round the edges of two big, fleshy leaves. They then "stitch" them together with bits of fiber. Inside the hanging cradle thus made they build a small, soft woolly nest.

Six widely differing kinds of nests which different species of bird build as the first step towards caring for their young ones.

Nests under Ground, Nests under Water

Birds are not by any means the only creatures which make homes for their young ones. The mole cricket, which looks like a thickset grasshopper, burrows into the earth and lays her eggs at the end of a tunnel. Until they hatch, she stays close beside them. After the young ones hatch out she stands near the mouth of the tunnel on the lookout for enemies. Rabbits also make an underground chamber for their young, the mother rabbit often lining part of it with her own fur to form a cozy nest. The prairie dogs of North America, squirrel-like animals, live together in great numbers, sometimes excavating hundreds of underground passages where they rear their young.

Under water, where there may be tides and currents to contend with, nest-building is probably a more difficult art than it is on dry land. Yet many water-dwellers manage to provide admirable protection for their eggs or homes for their young ones.

The sand goby seems to have hit on the simplest method. The male looks for an empty shell and maneuvers it until it rests like a tent on the sandy sea-bed. Then he makes a small tunnel through the sand leading into it. The female swims through the tunnel, lays her eggs inside the shell and goes away. The male fertilizes the eggs and then stays by the tunnel until they hatch.

Sticklebacks (top pictures), on the other hand, design and build their nests themselves. The active partner in nest-building is the male. First he makes quite a high pile of grass and water plants, and cements it together with a sticky excretion from his kidneys. Then he makes an entrance hole, swims inside, makes another hole to serve as exit, and goes out again. Next he waits near the nest until, by his graceful evolutions in the water he can persuade a female to enter it. After she has gone inside and laid her eggs she leaves the nest forever. But the male stickleback now enters it again, collects the scattered eggs together and fertilizes them. Then he stays by the nest not only until the young ones have hatched out, but until they are big enough not to need his protection any longer.

The rest of the pictures on the facing page show stages in the building of what is, perhaps, the most astonishing of all underwater nests, that of the water spider. This creature makes an underwater web shaped like a thimble and fixes it to water plants in such a way that the open end always points downward and the closed end upward. When the web is finished, the spider rises to the surface and maybe rests for awhile on a leaf. Then, with its two hairy back legs curving together, it dives down into the water again.

Trapped between those hairy legs it carries a small bubble of air with it. Directly under the web it releases the air, which rises to the closed top of the web and drives out some of the water. Over and over again the industrious spider goes to the surface and dives down again, each time carrying another air bubble on the return journey. In time all the water is driven out of the web and it is filled with air instead, just like a man-made diving-bell.

At the beginning of summer the spider lays her first batch of eggs. They hatch quickly and the young ones soon build tiny diving-bells of their own. In autumn a second batch of eggs is laid. But these do not hatch out at once. The mother spider seals her underwater nest and, keeping these eggs inside it with her, she hibernates. Not until she wakes up the following spring does her second batch of eggs hatch out. During the egg-laying period the male spider builds a diving-bell near that of the female, and a passage links the two together.

TOP: A female stickleback lays her eggs inside the nest the male has built. The male arranges the eggs, fertilizes them, then guards them. BOTTOM: The wonderful air-filled underwater nests of water spiders.

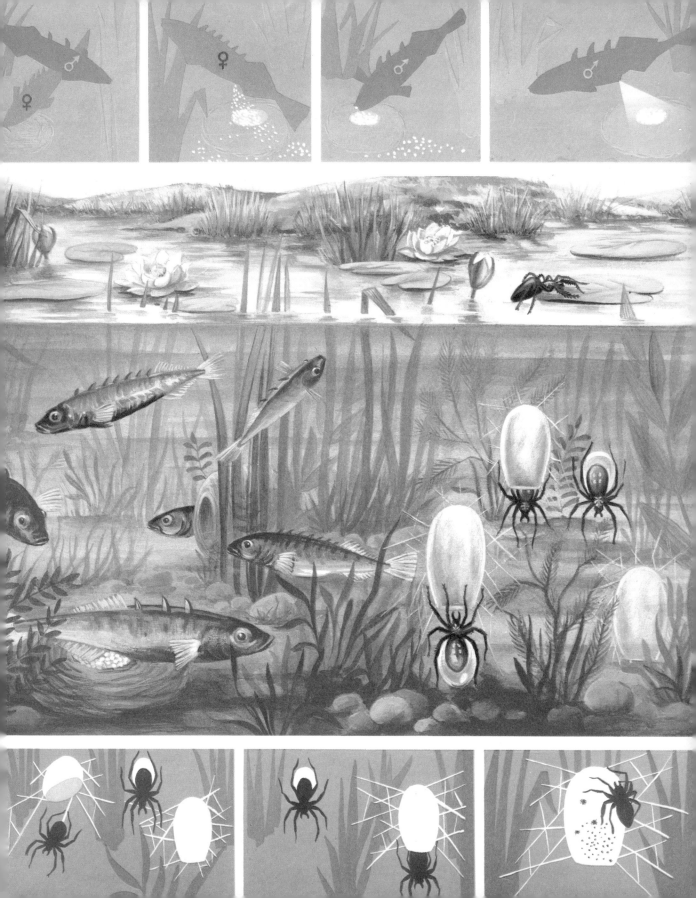

How Seeds Disperse and Grow

In autumn, when crops of grain are harvested, some of the ripe seed must be stored ready for next season's sowing. The following year new plants spring up, some of them many miles away from where the parent plants grew. In this case the seed is transported and sown by the agency of man. But few plants can rely on man to ensure the continuity of their species. Each seed-producing plant has some way of dispersing and sowing seed for itself.

Many of the methods of seed dispersal which nature has devised are strikingly similar to devices which man has invented — but only millions of years after the plants! The dandelion, for instance, carries its tiny seeds at the bottom of slender structures like small parachutes, and the lightest breeze can carry them great distances to new growing grounds. Sycamore seeds are attached to a pair of "wings" not unlike an airplane propeller. Not only are they easily carried by the wind, but also, when the seed falls, the wind sometimes continues to spin the "wings" round, helping to embed the seed firmly in the soft earth.

Some plants have seed-pods which in dry weather open rather like a hinged window-pane and disperse the seed through the opening. When the seed of a poppy becomes dry, the cap lifts and sprinkles the seeds out as we might sprinkle salt from a container. As the pod of the sweet pea dries, it shrivels and twists, finally shooting out the seeds as if from a spring gun.

Over the course of his long history man has ceased to rely on his own muscles to move all his goods from place to place, and has invented many other means of transport by land and water. Certain plants also enlist outside help in transporting their seeds. Sticky burrs containing seeds may cling to a dog's coat or a man's trouser-legs and be carried some distance from the plant on which they grew. The seeds of the parent coconut-palm are often carried from one tropical island to another by ocean currents. They are encased in the strong but light and hollow coconut which floats on the water just as strong but light and hollow ocean liners do.

Sometimes man takes plants to new, and even far-distant, growing grounds quite deliberately, in the course of experiments in agriculture. Blackberries were taken from Europe to Australia, tomatoes from America to Europe, and rubber-producing plants from South America to East Asia in this way. Often, too, man transports plants to new ground quite by accident — perhaps when loading up ships and trains. Tradition even has it that Caesar's legions brought the seeds of stinging nettles to Britain on the muddy soles of their boots.

By whatever means it is carried, a seed will germinate provided it finds suitable conditions of soil and climate. Though not all seeds make this first act of independent and individual growth in precisely the same way, the broad outline of the process is similar for most.

The bottom pictures show stages in the growth of a pumpkin. The seed is carried in the sticky pulp of the vegetable, so when it is planted the seed-envelope normally adheres easily to the soil. When germination begins, a radicle, or young root, penetrates the seed-envelope and pushes its way into the soil. Then the stem begins to develop, lifting what is left of the seed clear of the ground. Next the latter begins to open and the young seed-leaves make their appearance. Until these leaves are developed sufficiently to make enough food by means of photosynthesis, the young plant still draws on the food supply stored in the old, and now opened, seed. Sometimes, the pumpkin seed envelope does not adhere firmly to the soil. If it chances to shift about the radicle may not get a firm hold in the soil. In that case the young plant will probably die.

TOP: Six methods by which different plants disperse their seeds. Each reminds us of a different man-made device. BOTTOM: How a pumpkin plant grows from a seed.

The Mighty Thirst of Trees

From the moment a plant begins to grow it needs water. Water is the main ingredient of the sap, and the sap serves as the carrier and supply system of the plant, just as blood serves as the carrier and supply system in the body of an animal.

We saw earlier that the human body needs several pints of water every day, and we also noticed that it gives out approximately as much water as it takes in. A plant uses some of the water it takes in to combine with carbon-dioxide to make food. Nevertheless its leaves give out to the air a very high proportion of the water which its roots take in from the soil.

Scientists have carried out experiments to discover just how much water one fully-grown beech tree gives out in the course of a single summer. They have reached the astonishing conclusion that it is about 2,000 gallons. The top left-hand picture gives an idea of the size a water-tower would have to be to hold that much. If one acre of woodland contains 160 beech trees, they will thus give off some 320,000 gallons of water among them every summer. If that amount were spread evenly over the whole surface of the acre, it would flood it to a depth of about 14 inches. The top right-hand picture shows that such a depth of water would come nearly to the top of a man's shins.

These facts help us to appreciate why the indiscriminate felling of trees can be dangerous, especially when it is carried out on hillsides. When there is very heavy rain on a hillside, trees can *quickly* absorb much of it, and *gradually* return it to the air to take part in nature's great water-cycle once more. If the trees are all cut down, large quantities of water, which the soil cannot immediately absorb, will go coursing down the hillside, carrying precious top-soil away.

How does water travel many yards up a tree, from the tips of its roots to the highest leaves (as shown in the bottom left-hand picture)? The small root-hairs of the tree, which contain fairly thick fluid, are covered with a fine membrane. This membrane allows water to pass from the soil into the root, but it will not allow the thick fluid to pass from the root into the soil. Thus a pressure develops inside these roots, helping to push the water upwards. Next, the trunk, branches and twigs of the tree contain vast numbers of cells which form structures rather like very fine tubes, and the water level always tends to rise in any such fine tubes, or capillaries, whether they are made by nature or by man. Last of all, the leaves themselves are constantly losing water to the air by a process very similar to evaporation; in their efforts to replace it they act as thousands of tiny pumps, each helping to raise the water.

Water rises in different trees at different rates. The three light arrows in the bottom right-hand picture indicate how far the water rises in a pine, a poplar and an oak in a single hour. The figures of men emphasize the scale. In the pine, water rises at about three feet per hour; in the poplar, almost twenty feet; in the oak, almost thirty feet.

The reason for these differences lies in the structure of the trees. In the wood of a pine tree, for instance, all the cells are of a similar kind. Each must help to give the tree strength as well as to carry water, so all the cell-walls are somewhat thick. The wood of an oak tree, on the other hand, has cells of three different kinds: some like those of the pine, some fibrous strengthening cells, and other cells which specialize in carrying water. Further, water evaporates more rapidly from broad, fleshy oak leaves than from fine, leathery pine-needles.

TOP LEFT: The amount of water one beech tree gives out in one summer. TOP RIGHT: The depth of water which 160 beeches absorb from an acre of land. BOTTOM LEFT: Water climbs from roots to tree-top. BOTTOM RIGHT: How far water rises in different trees in one hour.

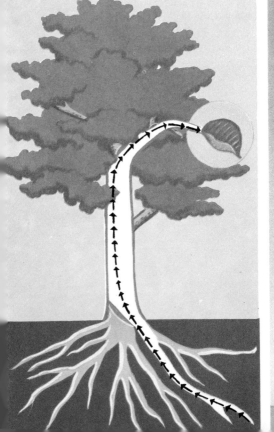

The Man Who Made Heredity a Science

For many centuries farmers tried to rear animals with certain outstanding characteristics, such as cows with a high milk yield, or sheep with long white fleeces, by carefully selecting the animals from which they bred. Although, over the years, they met with considerable success, they also met with numerous failures and surprises. That is because until comparatively recent times nobody really understood the natural mechanism by which such characteristics were transmitted.

The first man to make a rewarding scientific study of the subject was Gregor Mendel, who was born on a farm in 1822, and later became a monk and a teacher of natural history in a monastery at Brünn in Moravia. There, while devoting much of his time to tending the monastery garden, he embarked on a long series of controlled experiments to find out just how ordinary garden peas pass on various characteristics from generation to generation.

His most striking results came from crossing two kinds of pea, one which grew to a considerable height and one which was a dwarf variety. First he used the tall-growing peas as the "mother" plants, fertilizing their seeds with pollen from the dwarfs. Next he reversed the process, using seeds from the dwarfs and pollen from the tall plants. In both cases *all* the resulting plants were tall. Mendel repeated the experiment with many more plants, testing for one specific characteristic each time. The result was always the same. All the resulting individuals of the first generation of new plants were always identical.

Mendel thus recognized that different characteristics of plants do not all exercise an equal influence on the make-up of the next generation. Giant and dwarf parent peas do not contribute equally to be characteristics of the daughter peas; they do not produce plants of medium height. Mendel thus reasoned that some hereditary characteristics, such as tallness in peas, are *dominant*, while others, such as dwarfishness, are *recessive*, no matter which parent has the characteristic concerned. Thus Mendel established his first "law" which lays down that hybrids of the first generation are always alike and present the dominant characteristic. He also discovered, however, that recessive characteristics reappear in later generations.

In writing about heredity, biologists use the letter P (the initial of the Latin word *parentes*) to denote the two parents originally crossed. They use F (the initial of the Latin word *filia*, meaning daughter) to denote the generations which result from this crossing (F_1 for the first generation, F_2 for the second generation, and so on).

The series of flower pictures opposite shows that it is not true in every case that an hereditary characteristic must be either dominant or recessive. The flower shown, whose botanical name is *Mirabilis jalapa*, is an instance of where two characteristics of the parents *do* contribute equally to the make-up of the next generation, the redness of one parent and the whiteness of the other producing pinkness in the daughter plants. Such characteristics are called intermediate.

Of P, the two original parent plants which are crossed, one is red and the other white. All the individuals of the resulting generation, F_1, are alike and all are pink. If now, any two individuals of F_1 are crossed, they produce a generation F_2 in which a quarter of the individuals are red, half are pink, and the remaining quarter are white.

If two of the pink plants of F_2 are crossed they produce a generation, F_3, in which red flowers, pink flowers and white flowers occur in the proportion 1:2:1. But if two red flowers from F_2 are crossed they produce only red flowers in F_3. Similarly, if two white flowers from F_2 are crossed they produce only white flowers in F_3.

Although he lived at a time when far less was known about cell-structure than is known today, Mendel succeeded in explaining many important facts about heredity, but little attention was given to his explanations until about 1900, some sixteen years after his death.

TOP: Gregor Mendel, the gardener-monk who pioneered the study of heredity. OTHER PICTURES: Proportions of pink, red and white flowers grown in successive generations from one red and one white parent plant.

P

F

F

F3

Some of the Laws of Heredity

The laws of heredity which Mendel discovered hold good not only for plants but also for animals, man included. A human generation is measured at about a quarter of a century. To test Mendelian laws with human beings would therefore be an extremely slow process. But biologists have plentiful, quick-breeding material for such experiments in mice, for mice produce a new generation every few weeks.

If you crossed a pure-bred white mouse with a pure-bred black, you would soon realize that the *Mirabilis jalapa* pattern is repeated in the animal world. Irrespective of which parent is black and which is white, the offspring would all be grey. Our illustrations on the facing page show the parents again as P and the offspring as F1. If you mate two of the all-grey offspring, they will produce another generation, F2, made up of white, grey and black mice in the one-two-one proportion which we saw on the previous page. Thus the temporarily masked characteristics of the original black mouse and white mouse reappear in some of their grandchildren.

If you take the experiment further and mate the white grandchildren with each other you find they produce all-whites in F3; similarly if you mate the black grandchildren they produce all-blacks in F3. But if you mate two grey mice of the F2 generation, the one-two-one ratio turns up again in F3: one white, two grey, one black. You have not been able to breed true with your greys.

All this confirms two of Mendel's laws: (1) that first-generation hybrids of two pure-bred parents are identical, (2) that second-generation plants or animals produced from such hybrids are not identical. It is noteworthy that the one-two-one ratio in the F2 generation occurs only in cases where the hereditary characteristics concerned (*i.e.* the color characteristic in the mice, or the color characteristic in the *Mirabilis jalapa*) are neither dominant nor recessive, but intermediate. Where dominant and recessive characteristics are concerned, the grandchildren reveal their grandparents' characteristics in the ratio three-to-one: three corresponds to the "dominant" grandparent, one to the "recessive" grandparent.

You may also cross back with mice, mating a grey hybrid of the F1 generation with a pure black of the P generation. The result, as one might expect, is the same as what happens when the grey and the black mice (third example of F2 in the diagram) mate. That is, the offspring are one white, two grey, one black. If, however, the color black were a dominant characteristic, all the progeny of the grey-black mating would be black; if black were a recessive characteristic, only half the offspring of such a union would be black, and the other half would be white.

The illustrations of cattle show how Mendel's laws operate when the original parents are each distinguished from the other by *two* different hereditary color characteristics. The results reveal clearly which are the dominant and which the recessive color characteristics of the cattle concerned. In the diagrams, the black and red strips denote the color characteristics passed on by the original bull; green and blue strips indicate those passed on by the original cow. In the first generation, black dominates other colors and both bull and heifer calf have a uniform black coat. Yet, as the black, red, green and blue color keys show, both bull and heifer carry the mechanism for producing brown and spotted coats.

It is assumed that the bull and heifer (F1) are mated repeatedly and eventually become the parents of sixteen calves. The pictures show that nine are black, three are mainly black with brown patches, one is mainly brown with black patches, and three are all brown.

TOP: Successive generations from original pure-bred white mouse and pure-bred black mouse. Both color characteristics are intermediate. BOTTOM: Two generations of cattle from original parents, each of which has one dominant and one recessive color characteristic.

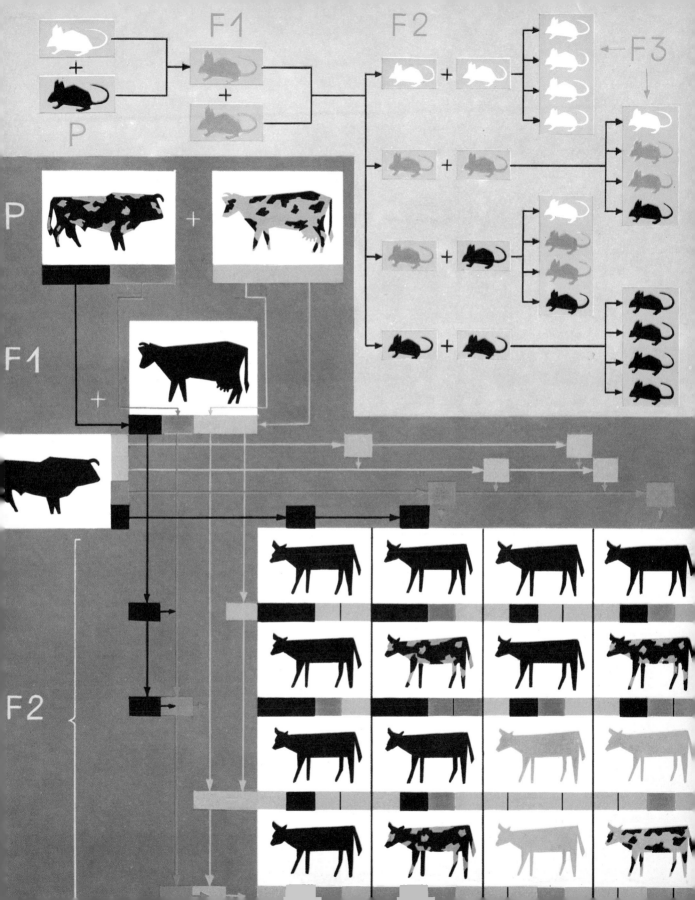

P

F1

F2

F3

Chromosomes, Moulders of the Future

Not until some years after Mendel did scientists actually discover the mechanism by which nature passes on hereditary characteristics. Then, using high-powered microscopes, they located it within the nucleus of the living cell. Their observations showed that when a cell is about to divide, its nucleus contains a number of short, thick, rod-shaped structures. These are chromosomes. Later it was discovered that the nucleus of the living cell when not in process of dividing contains chromosomes in the form of fine threads. It is the chromosomes which pass on family likenesses.

Biologists have established that each species has its own special number. The left-hand side of the opposite page shows the count for each of sixteen different species. One might imagine that the higher animals possess more chromosomes than the lower animals, but this is not so. In fact, there is no obvious connection between an animal's chromosome-count and its size or position on the ladder of evolution.

We saw earlier that sex cells contain only half as many chromosomes as do ordinary body-cells. It is therefore not surprising that all the sixteen species shown opposite, which reproduce sexually, have an *even* number of chromosomes in their ordinary body-cells. Man's body-cells possess 46 — two pairs of 23 — as shown in the top illustration. In a man the last pair consists of one X and one Y chromosome; in a woman, of two X chromosomes. This last pair determines the sex of the individual.

This relation between sex and chromosomes is also true in the *Drosophila melanogaster*, or banana fly (center right), studied by the American scientist, T. H. Morgan. The banana fly possesses four pairs of chromosomes which differ considerably in appearance. It is the ideal creature for the expert on heredity to study because it is small, breeds rapidly, is easy to raise in tubes containing boiled banana, and can be drugged with ether without suffering any serious after effects. Finally, its salivary gland cells contain giant chromosomes, ideal for microscopic examination.

Morgan found that these chromosomes consist largely of discs piled irregularly on one another, as shown in the vastly magnified representation beside his portrait. These discs are genes, and by patient observation and study Morgan was able to show that each gene exercises its own fixed influence on one particular physical characteristic.

In the chromosomes, the genes seemed to be arranged always in much the same fashion. Moreover, the number of genes seemed to correspond with the number of hereditary characteristics which could be observed in the insect. Morgan's work proved beyond reasonable doubt that the presence or absence of certain genes determines the presence or absence of certain characteristics in the banana fly. He found it possible to isolate the genes controlling large or small eyes, large or small wings, etc. In time it was thus possible to build up a chart showing which of many characteristics was determined by which of many genes.

If a chromosome contained, for example, both the gene for red eyes and the gene for small wings, Morgan would examine the descendants of the parents which bore these genes to see if the effects of both appeared together in those descendants. Sometimes they did not. It sometimes happens that two genes present in a chromosome are not closely linked. In that case, during the formation of sex cells (which contain only one set of chromosomes, instead of a pair of sets), two genes which were previously in the same chromosome may finish up in two different ones. Thus the gene for red eyes may end up in a different chromosome from the gene for small wings. But if two genes are close to one another in a chromosome it is far more likely that they will remain linked than that they will become separated.

TOP: Chromosomes in a man and a woman. LEFT: Chromosome-counts for sixteen different species. CENTER RIGHT: Chromosome pattern for male and female banana fly. BOTTOM RIGHT: T. H. Morgan and the gene make-up of a chromosome.

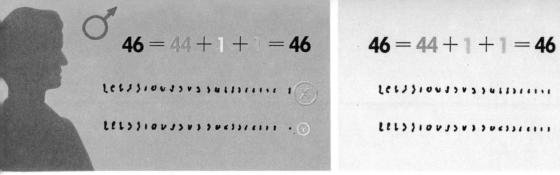

$$46 = 44 + 1 + 1 = 46 \qquad 46 = 44 + 1 + 1 = 46$$

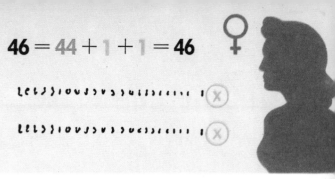

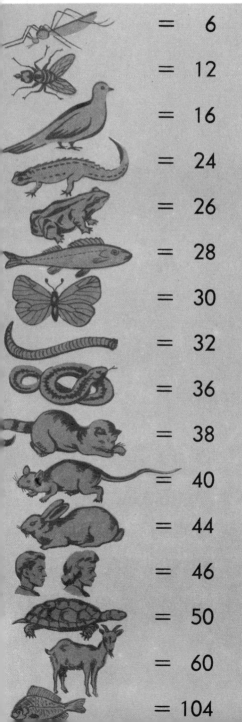

	= 6
	= 12
	= 16
	= 24
	= 26
	= 28
	= 30
	= 32
	= 36
	= 38
	= 40
	= 44
	= 46
	= 50
	= 60
	= 104

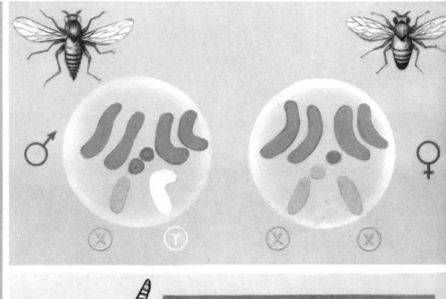

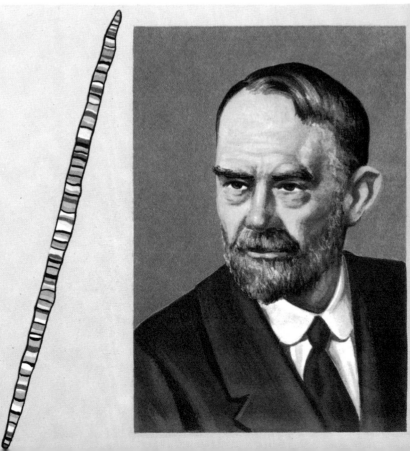

Boy or Girl — What are the Chances?

Chromosomes not only control the great variety of characteristics we inherit, including color of eyes and hair, shape of nose, and to some extent temperament and character; they also determine our sex.

We noticed on the last page that of the 46 chromosomes which men and women possess in their body-cells, 44 — arranged as two pairs of 22 — are common to both sexes. In a woman the remaining chromosomes also form a true pair, consisting of two more or less identical X chromosomes. But in a man the last two chromosomes are not a true pair, one being termed X and the other Y. It is this difference in the last "pair" of chromosomes which determines the sex of the individual.

The small grey circles in the diagram opposite all show ordinary body-cells, greatly simplified. Green indicates X chromosomes, yellow Y chromosomes, and black the remaining ones. We must now pause and think what happens when such cells divide in a special way to form reproductive cells. These reproductive cells do not contain 23 *pairs* of chromosomes but simply 23 *individual* chromosomes. Thus, in a woman, the reproductive cells will always contain 22 ordinary chromosomes and 1 X chromosome. But in a man the reproductive cells may contain *either* 22 ordinary and 1 X, *or* 22 ordinary and 1 Y.

If a male reproductive cell *of the first kind* unites with a female reproductive cell, the resulting fertilized cell will therefore contain 44 ordinary and 2 X chromosomes, and the child to which it gives rise will be a girl. But if a male reproductive cell *of the second kind* unites with a female reproductive cell, the resulting fertilized cell will contain 44 ordinary, 1 X, and 1 Y chromosomes, and the child will be a boy. You can check nature's arithmetic against the top diagram on the previous page.

When a new addition to the family is expected, the question which has always loomed large is "Will it be a boy or a girl?" Some centuries ago it was a general practice, when a girl married, for her parents to give her husband a dowry — a very substantial present of money or goods. If parents not overblessed with wealth had several daughters the practice was sometimes ruinously expensive. So it is hardly surprising that insuring against the birth of a daughter was one of the earliest forms of insurance. The sixteenth-century merchants who agreed to pay out if a daughter was born had to have some idea of what the chances were in order to charge a fair premium. Usually they made a bold guess that the chances were about fifty-fifty, and charged accordingly.

At that time there were no thoroughly reliable and complete registers of births, and their guess *was* only a guess. But it was a surprisingly good one. Now that we do have reliable registers, we can say with certainty that, over a long period and throughout a great part of the world, the number of girls born every year is very nearly equal to the number of boys. For every 100 girls born there are 105 boys born.

Until comparatively recent times it was still fashionable to refer to women as "the weaker sex", and to men as "the stronger sex". If we think only about lifting-power and muscular development there is some justification for these terms. But in fact it is women who have the greater resistance to disease, and the greater ability to recuperate from illness, and statistics show that in all civilized countries a woman's expectation of life exceeds a man's by several years.

It is easy to stress the considerable physical differences between men and women — robustness of skeleton, degree of muscular development, amount of facial hair, pitch of voice and so on — and to overlook the fact that both men and women share many characteristics in common, characteristics which are neither distinctively male nor distinctively female, but quite distinctly human.

The X (green) and Y (yellow) chromosomes determine sex. A child always inherits one X from its mother. From its father it inherits either an X or a Y. If the former it is a girl, if the latter a boy.

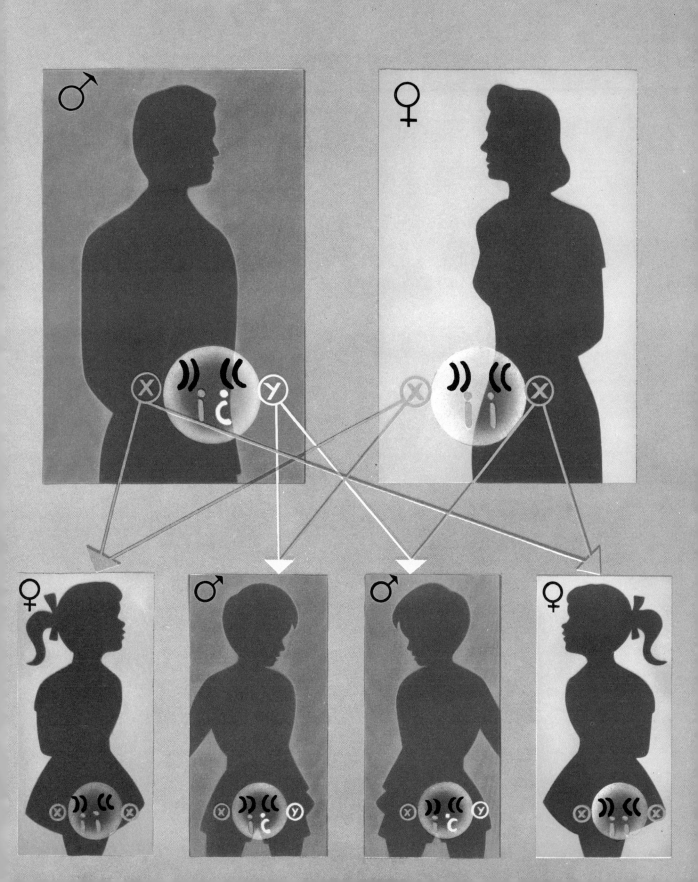

Tracking Down Diseases of the Blood

Some years ago doctors carried out, for the first time, a desperate and astonishing experiment with a newly-born jaundiced baby who was in danger of dying. By transfusion, they replaced the whole of the blood in its body. The sick child soon assumed a normal color, its breathing improved, and its life was saved. The experiment was connected with the mysterious rhesus factor which scientists had just discovered.

The story of the discovery begins with the work of Dr. Landsteiner, whose research into blood groups has already been mentioned. In 1937 Dr. Landsteiner and his associate, Dr. A. S. Wiener (top right), examined the blood of a rabbit into which had been injected a little blood from a rhesus monkey (pictured top left). They found that a new chemical substance had formed in the rabbit's blood plasma. They called it Rh, from the name of the rhesus monkey. Dr. Wiener asked himself whether human blood also contained this substance. He embarked on exhaustive researches and arrived at the conclusion that some 85 per cent of people possess this Rh substance in their blood.

At first his conclusions aroused only a very limited interest in the scientific world. No one was as yet able to assess their practical value. Fortunately, Dr. Wiener conceived the idea of concentrating on cases of blood transfusion which had not succeeded or had even resulted in the death of the patient; for although, by this time, incompatible blood groups were never mingled in the course of transfusion, it still occasionally happened that a patient had a bad reaction or even died. The cause might possibly lie in mixing blood which contained the Rh substance with blood which did not. Suspicion rapidly changed into certainty. When Rh-positive blood is mixed with Rh-negative blood, a violent reaction may in certain circumstances occur, a reaction which destroys many red blood cells. Severe illness and even death may result.

A year or two after Dr. Wiener's discoveries, another scientist, Dr. Levine, concentrated on the characteristics of a peculiar illness which attacked newly born, and even unborn, children. The disease was characterized by the destruction of red blood cells. Dr. Levine suspected that it might be caused when women with Rh-negative blood had children whose blood, inherited from the father, was Rh-positive. In such cases the blood of the mother could, in certain circumstances, enter into conflict with the blood of her own child. Over a considerable period the blood of both parents of children suffering from the disease was tested. In each case it was found that the mother was Rh-negative and the father Rh-positive.

Thus the rhesus factor not only explained failures which sometimes occurred during blood transfusion, it also threw new light on an illness which had previously cost the lives of many children. Doctors now know that an Rh-negative woman married to an Rh-positive man can have healthy children. The danger arises only when and if the mother becomes sensitized to the Rh factor.

Most diseases have nothing to do with heredity, but a few, including the one just described, most certainly have. To deal with such diseases effectively, and to know when to expect them, medical men need to understand just how they are handed on. The bottom part of the opposite page shows how the characteristic of albinism (marked by red eyes) is passed on through several generations of rabbits. The letter **a** printed in red indicates the presence of the gene which determines this characteristic. Only where **aa** printed in red is shown in the same individual does albinism actually occur.

The infantile disease connected with the rhesus factor is handed on among human beings according to a very similar pattern.

TOP: The species of monkey from which the rhesus factor takes its name. Proportions of Rh-positive and Rh-negative people. Dr. Wiener, who pioneered work on the rhesus factor. BOTTOM: How albinism is passed on among rabbits. Certain inherited diseases are passed on in a similar hereditary pattern.

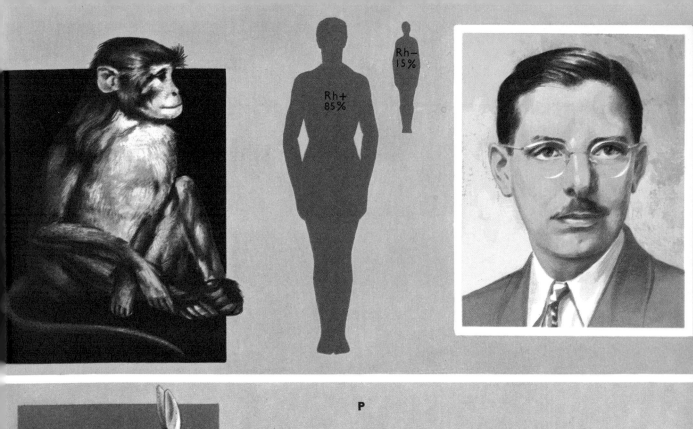

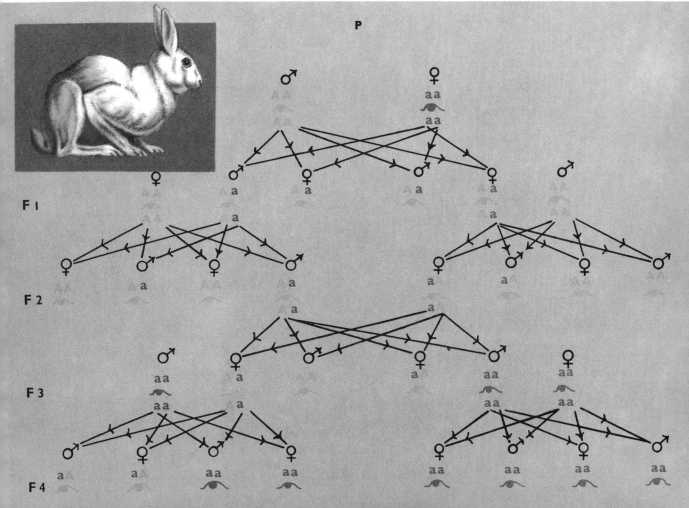

P

♂ ♀
AA aa
AA aa

♀ ♂ ♀ ♂ ♀ ♂
F 1 a a a a a a
AA AA AA
a a

♀ ♂ ♀ ♂ ♀ ♂ ♀ ♂
F 2 AA a AA a a a AA
a a

♂ ♀ ♀ ♂ a ♀ ♂
F 3 aa a a aa aa
aa aa aa

♂ ♀ ♂ ♀ ♀ ♂ ♀ ♂
F 4 aA aA aa aa aa aa aa aa

The Inheritance of Ability

Scientists can carry out many experiments on heredity with fast-breeding plants and animals which they can conveniently study at close quarters. But studying heredity in man is more difficult, for he lives so long, produces fresh generations so slowly, and does not lend himself to the continued scrutiny of the biologist. To learn about heredity in man, the biologist must therefore make use of indirect sources of information. He can, for instance, study family trees or follow the separate development of identical twins.

Few of us know much about our forebears, biologically speaking. We may know what trades or professions several of our ancestors followed, and we may have portraits of some of them. Even this information is often limited to our male ancestors, which is a pity, for women play an equal part with men in passing on characteristics.

Luckily, however, we know a good deal about the descent of several famous men. Our illustrations show family trees for two of them: the great naturalist, Charles Darwin (above), and the great composer, Johann Sebastian Bach (below). Darwin was exceptionally endowed with a brilliant analytical mind. Bach is often regarded as the greatest of all composers of music. Each had a particular kind of ability inherited from his ancestors and passed on to his descendants. You can see how this ability recurs in both the family trees. Red indicates that the ability was so marked as to entitle its possessor to the appellation of genius; green denotes ability of a very high order; blue denotes at least the obvious possession of ability.

In each family, the most famous member was certainly not the *only* famous one. Charles Darwin's grandfather, Erasmus Darwin, was a well-known biologist, especially interested in heredity. Charles Darwin's cousin, Sir Francis Galton (also a grandson of Erasmus), became a world-famous biologist, and incidentally the pioneer of identifying people by their fingerprints.

Two of Charles Darwin's sons also achieved great distinction, Sir Francis as a plant physiologist, and Sir George as an astronomer. Of course we cannot be certain just how big a part was played by the women who married into the Darwin family and who brought up the children, but we can be fairly sure that upbringing, as well as heredity, played a part in the way they developed their gifts.

Bach's family tree is just as interesting as Darwin's. Bach was married twice, first to his cousin, a musically gifted woman, and second to a woman with no musical gifts. Again, the children of both marriages were all gifted.

Unfortunately undesirable characteristics can be inherited no less than desirable ones. Criminal tendencies, a few forms of mental ill-health, alcoholism — all can be handed on in a family. People often ask whether heredity or environment creates a criminal. Often the answer is both. To help solve such problems, scientists can study the separate development of identical twins.

So far as inherited characteristics go, identical twins truly are identical. Thus as they grow up, any differences which appear between them must be due to the effects of environment. One twin may have a completely different education from the other; one may grow up in a town, the other in the country. Such differences can affect their tastes and habits to such an extent that they develop into two very different people.

In countless ways science is making living conditions easier for all of us. Modern hygiene, modern knowledge of diet, modern medicine, ensure that many people who once would have failed early in the competition for survival, now reach maturity and have children of their own. Sometimes this means that weaklings and mentally deficient people have as good a chance as healthy people of passing on their characteristics. Thus, though science solves many problems, it can also create new ones.

ABOVE: Family tree of the Darwins includes Erasmus Darwin (A), Charles Darwin (B), Sir Francis Galton (C). BELOW: Family tree of the Bachs. In both trees red indicates exceptional ability, green remarkable ability, and blue marked ability.

Darwin and the Origin of Species

Throughout by far the greater part of human history, the majority of people believed that all the many species of plants and animals had existed unchanged from the moment of their creation, and that each species represented a separate act of creation. Such a belief would have been both simple and satisfying if there had been no evidence to the contrary. But in fact there was some such evidence. Man himself, by carefully selecting the plants and animals from which he bred, had changed many species almost out of recognition. Was it not therefore possible that under natural conditions over a far longer period, even more had occurred?

The tremendous importance of Charles Darwin's work lies not only in the fact that he showed that under natural conditions such profound changes can and do occur, but that also suggested clearly how they are brought about. No other work has produced such an impact on scientists as his book "The Origin of Species by Natural Selection", which appeared in 1859. Other scientists had explored the subject but none had assembled such formidable evidence.

Charles Darwin (above) based many of his findings on his observations of pigeons. At that time pigeon breeding was extremely popular in England. There existed more than 150 different breeds, some of them so different from others that one might believe them to be quite different species. Yet every one of them is descended from the rock pigeon.

Darwin asked himself how the pigeon breeders had reached such a result. Three circumstances seemed to him to be decisive in the success they had achieved: a certain mutability, or variation of characteristics, often observed in the descendants of a single pair of pigeons; the fact that such variations can be handed on; the fact that the breeders had carefully selected their stock birds.

Something of the mechanism which enabled the breeders to produce new strains is shown in the illustration opposite. By mating two birds, both of which had a tendency towards a slim, smooth body-outline (indicated by blue rings) they could intensify that characteristic in the next generation. By mating two birds of the generation which showed this characteristic in intensified form, they could intensify it still further, and so on, until they produced the typical carrier pigeon. Similarly, by choosing birds with other characteristics, they had been able to produce the fantail, the tumbler, the pouter, and many others.

Darwin next set out to answer the following question: If under natural conditions there have been produced similar but even greater changes in various animals and plants, what agency played the part corresponding to that of the pigeon breeder?

He came to the firm conclusion that the environment "selects" which creatures shall and which creatures shall not breed, and so pass on their inborn characteristics, by the test of which can best survive in a given environment. In nature all living things have a struggle to survive. They must successfully adapt themselves to heat or cold, drought or flood, predators and disease, hunger and thirst, and many other hazards. Darwin held that a characteristic which helps its possessor in the struggle for life is far more likely to be passed on than a characteristic which hinders. Creatures which have helpful characteristics are highly likely to reach maturity and to become parents of young ones with similar characteristics. Creatures with hindering characteristics frequently die young, and so fail to pass those characteristics on.

Occasionally drastic changes, of a kind not even yet fully understood, take place in the genes during reproduction. In such cases the offspring may be so different from the parent as to constitute the first of a new species. If the new species is better fitted to its environment than the old, it may, over many generations, completely replace the old one.

Charles Darwin recognized that "fancy" pigeons are all descendants of the rock pigeon (top). Each was produced by repeatedly selecting breeding birds with a particular characteristic (indicated by colors), and so intensifying it. He offered an explanation of how nature selects for breeding.

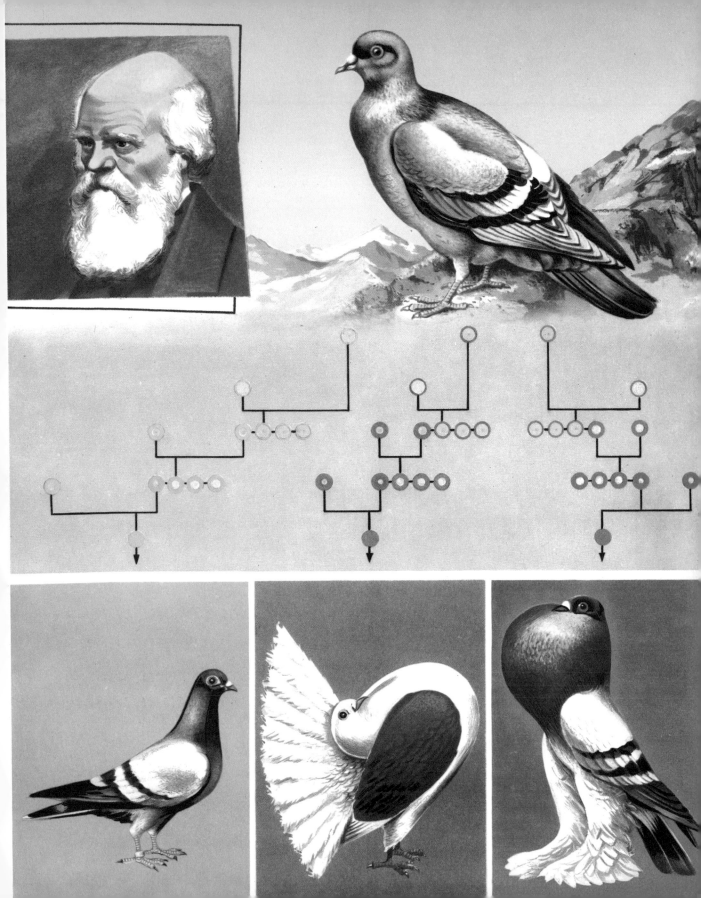

Living Fossils

Darwin's theory of natural selection not only explained how the living plants and animals of today came into being; it also explained how many extinct species came to die out. Long before Darwin's time people had puzzled over the imprints of strange ferns found in coal and over giant skeletons or fossil sea shells discovered deep under the earth's crust or high among mountain peaks.

Why had many of the creatures which left these remains died out? The answer often lies in changing environment. The climate may become too cold, too hot, too wet or too dry for them. If they cannot adapt themselves in time to new conditions they die out and other, better-adapted creatures take their place.

The earth's crust is made up of many different kinds and many different layers of rock, all formed at different periods. In a sense we may regard these rocks as the pages of a book, and the fossil remains they contain as the writing on them. Geologists can tell us the age of each rock or page, and naturalists can identify the creatures which left their remains, or made the writing, on each page. Thus we can read a fairly clear story of the immensely long history of living things. But we have to remember that many soft-bodied creatures with neither shells nor bones may have lived and died without leaving any lasting record in the book of the rocks.

From this record, scientists have estimated that, on an average, each species continues more or less unchanged for about a million years. Yet it sometimes happens that the life-span of a species is vastly longer than that. Indeed, some species which left their writings in the book of the rocks tens of millions or even hundreds of millions of years ago, still survive to this day. We may rightly think of such creatures as living fossils. Four living fossils, not all of equal antiquity, are shown on the facing page.

The nautilus (top left) is a mollusk found mainly in warm coastal waters of the Pacific and Indian Oceans, where it lives principally on the sea-floor, about 150 feet below water. It is only one of many living fossils in those waters, for it is estimated that some ten per cent of all species of mollusk found along the coasts of Java have existed for more than twenty-five million years.

Fishes with lungs first lived some three hundred million years ago and were probably among the first backboned animals to attempt to live on dry land. Many of them have long since disappeared but three species still survive, one in Africa, one in South America and one in Australia. The bottom left-hand picture shows an Australian lung-fish. During droughts, when water-courses dry up, it ceases to use its gills, hides in the mud, and breathes with its lungs.

Sphenodons (top right), a small group of lizard-like reptiles now found only on certain off-shore islands of New Zealand, have changed little if at all since before the age of the dinosaurs. These small burrowing creatures possess not only ordinary ribs, but also ribs which surround the abdomen and are unattached to the spine.

One kind of fossil skeleton, found in the Near and Middle East and dating back to more than five million years ago, long attracted attention. It seemed to be the remains of a biggish mammal with two small horns, and appeared to have been a link between the giraffe and the antelope. In 1900, in the forests of the Congo, Sir Harry Johnston discovered just such an animal still very much alive — the okapi (bottom right). Though it has no visible horns the male still has two rudimentary horns under the skin of the forehead.

Natural selection operates among living fossils no less than among other creatures. But they have long since been so well adapted to their surroundings that, over countless generations, only the characteristics which made them so have been handed on.

Four living fossils — creatures of a kind which have remained unchanged for millions of years. TOP LEFT: Nautilus. TOP RIGHT: Sphenodon. BOTTOM LEFT: Lung-fish. BOTTOM RIGHT: Okapi.

In this book we have delved into the mysteries of life in all its forms, from the lowliest of the plants to the highest of the animals — man himself. Yet amidst all its complexities and diversities we see a unifying thread running through the varied pattern — the creation of new life, its growth to maturity, its preparation of the next generation, and then decay and death. Man in his researches has discovered many facts about materials and machines. Now he is applying his ingenious instruments to the study of life itself, a study which has yielded fruitful results in our own lifetime. Will he discover the secret of life, the vital factor that makes us move, think, feel, love, hate and wonder? And if he does, what use will he make of it? Only in a world of people who are imbued with a sense of the wonder of life can such knowledge be safe for mankind.

Index